ARTISTS & ANATOMISTS

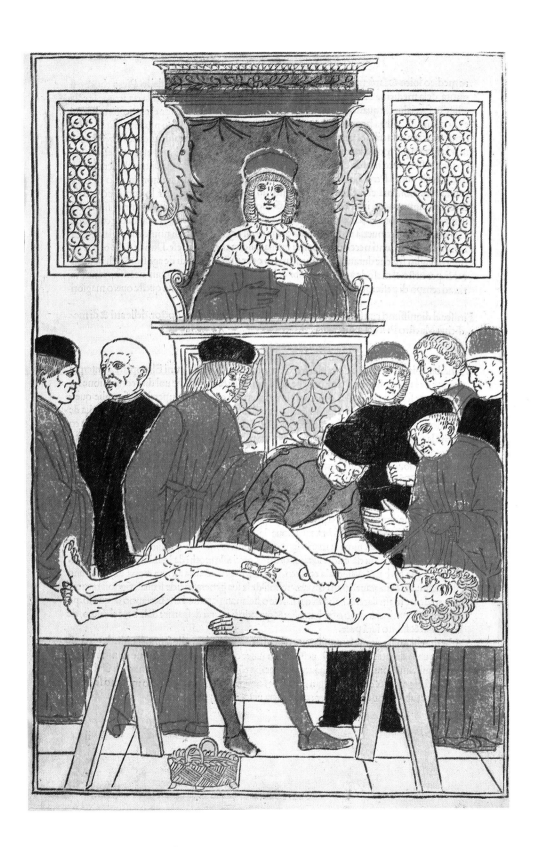

ARTISTS
&
ANATOMISTS

BY

A. HYATT MAYOR

PUBLISHED BY THE ARTIST'S LIMITED EDITION
IN ASSOCIATION WITH
THE METROPOLITAN MUSEUM OF ART

The publication of this edition of
"Artists & Anatomists"
was made possible by a grant
from U S V Laboratories.

CONTENTS

ARTISTS & ANATOMISTS

A. HYATT MAYOR *was Curator of Prints at The Metropolitan Museum of Art from 1946 to 1966. He wrote the manuscript for this book about 1954 at the urging of colleagues and friends who saw with new eyes after visiting an exhibition he had prepared on the same subject.*

Histories of anatomy exist in sufficient quantity, so this essay revolves around two questions only: What have artists done to record dissections and so help anatomists to see? And what, in turn, have anatomists discovered to help artists in portraying man's body? These questions center on the everlasting preoccupation of Western art, which is the study of man. They are part of one question today when some artists and all doctors study anatomy for structure and action, but before the Renaissance anatomists and artists were aware of each other only in oddly indirect ways.   A. H. M.

THE FAR EAST

QUESTIONS of anatomy occur to us so naturally that we find it hard to imagine a part of mankind that ignores them. So it might be good to begin by eliminating the vastness of the Far East, where artists tend to disregard anatomy because man blocks their view less than he does with us. In a typical Chinese landscape a philosopher contemplates from a far pavilion, or a fisherman poles a distant skiff because the picture requires an eye somewhere to bring the immensity of nature into the focus of an imagination. An artist needs no anatomy to paint man as the essential speck in a valley. So it is interesting to glance at the great arts that developed in lands where few bothered to uncover man's muscles or bones.

The Chinese are said to have dissected beggars and brigands in about A.D. 100–150 and again about 1150, but whatever they may have observed, they balked at applying their discoveries to the superior organism of the gentleman-scholar. (Only common people had hairy hearts.) Even after some Chinese had begun modern dissection in the early 19th century, most Chinese continued to have vague notions of anatomy, for Yu Li-tch'ou then said that missionaries would give up and go home if they had the sense to realize that they could never convert a people like the Chinese whose hearts grow on the right side. The only Chinese who could be christianized were the few freaks whose hearts grew on the left like the barbarians.

The Chinese illustrated their guides for the elaborate care of their health with diagrams of the digestive tract—fantasies in soft plumbing coiled within the outline of a human torso, which could well have been invented from opened animals (fig. 1). In about 1785 some Japanese compared these grave Chinese whimsies with the illustrations in a European anatomy book which they had smuggled into the country through the Dutch merchants at Deshima. The two kinds of pictures differed so totally that the Japanese decided to risk a test of truth by stealing the body of an executed

3

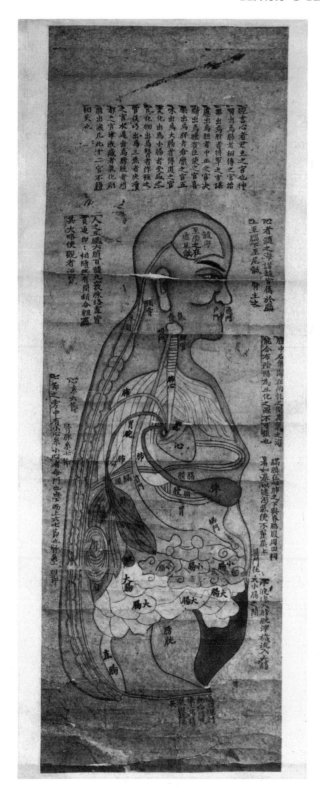

Fig. 1. Chinese anatomical chart, Ming period.
Wellcome Institute Library, London

Fig. 2. Japanese guardian figure, 13th century.
Courtesy of the Freer Gallery of Art Library,
Smithsonian Institution, Washington, D.C.

Fig. 3. Katsushika Hokusai, 1760–1849. Woodcut illustration from the *Manga* (Sketches), vol. 8.
The Metropolitan Museum of Art, New York.
The Howard Mansfield Collection, Gift of Howard Mansfield, 1936

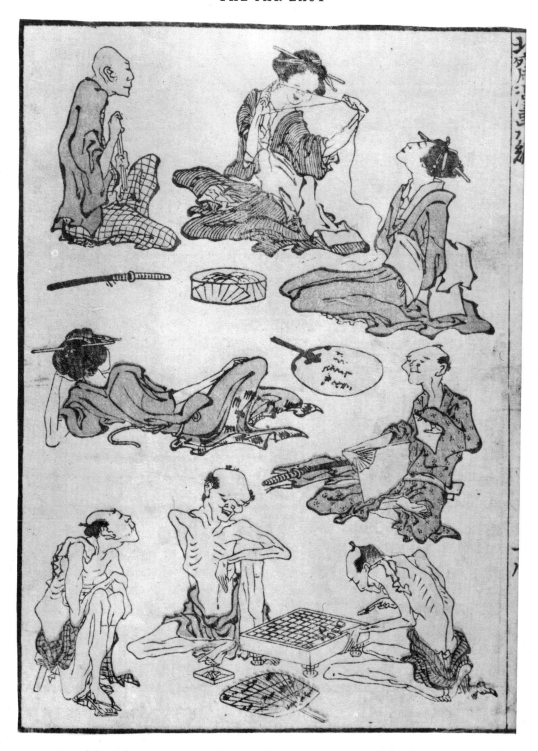

Fig. 4. Katsushika Hokusai, 1760–1849. Woodcut illustration from the *Manga* (Sketches), vol. 8.
The Metropolitan Museum of Art, New York.
The Howard Mansfield Collection, Gift of Howard Mansfield, 1936

criminal and opening it with both books at hand. When they uncovered organs that looked exactly like the European engravings and not at all like the Chinese diagrams, their experiment started the immense and fruitful Japanese production of all sorts of illustrated how-to-do-it books which have enabled them to catch up with Western technology and often to surpass it.

The Japanese assimilated our mechanics faster than our anatomy. Jiro Moroshima's *Komozakki* (Encyclopedia of Western Art and Science) published in Edo in 1787, has sixteen pages of woodcuts copied after European drawing books ranging from Dürer to the eighteenth century. Some of the cuts show how to lay out heads by drawing circles, a guide to proportion that must have looked to the Japanese like their parlor game of inventing pictures on chance lines and scribbles. But the *Komozakki* shows no internal construction of the figure, no dissections, and no skeleton. The Japanese seized on the externals of Western art without realizing the preliminary studies necessary to build up the end result. In this they acted just as we did when we first saw Japanese prints, or as anybody does when discovering an unfamiliar achievement.

The traditional Japanese way of seeing appears in a 13th century sculpture where realistic but random arm muscles fail to connect in any functional system, and something like a backbone divides the chest between the ribs (fig. 2). The "real" wrestler muscles contradict the devil mask of a face. Yet the Japanese often achieve originality and beauty when they juxtapose sharply seen detail with traditional patterns by twining flowers among geometric lattice.

The earliest outstanding Japanese artist who adapted elements of Western art was Hokusai. Perhaps because he was the first, he showed an Oriental indifference to anatomical function in his drawing book, the *Mangwa* (begun 1812), where he offered painting students a page of fat people and another of thin people (figs. 3, 4). The fat people float as confidently as balloons because their inflation conceals internal structure, but the skinny people show up his inadequate preparation for naturalism by collapsing in a jackstraw jumble of misunderstood bones.

Far Eastern art has almost always surpassed the West in exquisiteness, for few are the Westerners like Simone Martini who can challenge the Orient's swirling delicacy. The Chinese—and even more the Japanese—have been freer than we to finish surfaces, to match colors, to devise patterns, and to elaborate brush strokes for suggesting pines, carp, or rocks because they were not distracted by our exploratory drive to cut into man's body and to get inside the construction of space through mathematical perspective. Anatomy and perspective jolt us in the West with raw revelations of bone, muscle, and geometry, and thus puzzle us with problems so inexhaustible that we cannot imagine their ever ending. By ignoring these problems Oriental art gained the serenity that comes from contemplating the harmonies of nature instead of investigating the inner conflicts of man. Inevitably they must see our art as violent and vulgar, as we must see theirs as decorative and remote. But now that Western anatomical studies and mathematical perspective have permeated the whole world, how will they affect the East? Must they not unsettle the Oriental's immemorial mastery of flat pattern?

THE NEAR EAST

Our Western anatomical investigations began, like so much of our technology, in the ancient Near East, where the earliest recorded dissectors were the Babylonian soothsayers who read the will of the gods by inspecting sheep's viscera. They probably chose to open the belly of the sheep rather than, say, the leg because the bones and muscles of a leg remain the same from individual to individual, whereas intestines are free to coil and flow. The Akkadians connected dissection and prophecy so closely that they used almost the same word for "flesh" and "omen." They foresaw that a usurper would seize power from the king if the sheep's entrails resembled the face of Humbaba, a demon who lived among "steep climbs" and "barred paths" in the depths of a vast forest, like the Minotaur in the midst of his labyrinth. The real Humbaba may have been a volcano, for the Epic of Gilgamesh says that his cry is a hurricane, his mouth is fire, and his breath death. Babylonian priests used clay models of his terrible face (the original of the Gorgon's) to check against the entrails that they opened in the course of business (fig. 5). Humbaba's features of folded gut are not a decorative fantasy like the shell masks in baroque gardens; they are as practical as a yardstick. This seems to be art's first record of dissection. Thousands of years had to elapse before dissection began to affect art.

To the Babylonians, the "fortress of the bowels" surrounded the liver the way a city surrounds

Fig. 5. The demon Humbaba. Old Babylonian, 18th–17th century B.C. Terracotta relief. British Museum, London

9

its temple, so that the central liver, being the biggest organ and incorporating huge blood vessels, appeared to be the source of life. It thought and felt; it invigorated the whole body, until a passionate Babylonian (or anyone in the Near East today) might properly say "I love you with all my liver." The Babylonians inscribed clay models of livers with the description and meaning of each spot and crack. Etruscans copied these clay models in bronze when liver divination spread through the Mediterranean, where it persisted until Christian opposition.

The Babylonians did not extend their knowledge of sheep's anatomy to infer man's anatomy by similarity because they believed in a different analogy of man which survived them to sidetrack medicine until the Renaissance. This was the unhelpful misconception of our body as the little counterpart of the great structure of the constellations. Now if you think that a hostile conjunction of planets has made you break your leg, you naturally ask for guidance from an astrologer and not from a physician. Since error never dies, many people today still see themselves as puppets of the stars, even though Copernican astronomy has made it hard for us to liken man's body to the unimaginable galaxies.

EGYPT

EGYPTIANS and Greeks also dissected in their various ways. Egyptian embalmers seem to have been the first men to make a practice of opening other men, even though theirs was a mere ignorant ritual of evisceration, for after removing organs they sorted them into four jars with no further inquiry. While this process did not affect art in any way, both the embalmer and the sculptor worked for the same purpose in Egypt, for both enabled a man to live after his death, either by rendering his body incorruptible or by copying him from head to foot in a likeness adjusted to fit his ghost more snugly than our best cut clothes fit our bodies (fig. 6). The Egyptian sculptor's tailor-like scrutiny of a particular individual made him a more faithful portraitist than any Greek. But since the Egyptian cared nothing for muscle and bone as things of interest in themselves, he made bodies that are as lifelike as photographs of nudes, but which disappoint our eye the way photographs do because they lack the intellectual scheme of accent and articulation that Greek sculpture has trained us to expect in representations of the nude.

The failure of the unalerted eye to detect structure in an actual nude person, and the conscious effort needed to organize a living figure into a work of art are both sensitively stated in Charles-Antoine Jombert's treatise on drawing of 1755: "A beginner sees almost no muscles in a nude body, so before starting to draw the model you should acquire some smattering of anatomy to enable you to discover the whereabouts of the bones and muscles. I do not mean that you should draw all the muscles that you cannot see in the model just because you know they must be there."

Fig. 6. Statue of Khnumbaef. Egypt,
ca. 2440 B.C. Limestone.
The Metropolitan Museum of Art, New York.
Fletcher Fund, 1964

GREEK ANATOMISTS

THE Greeks were the first men to dissect for pure investigation. After the earliest Greeks had followed the Babylonians by opening sacrificial cattle for the ritual of forecasting, Aristotle (384–322 B.C.) turned ritual into science when he started toward the end of his life to dissect farm animals and monkeys in order to guess at man's insides by analogy. It is not quite certain just when Greeks started to dissect men, but they certainly did not do so commonly until pupils of Aristotle's pupils came to Alexandria about half a century after the master's death and there saw Egyptian embalmers opening bodies with unconcern. Once the Alexandrian anatomists had started on corpses, they dared further than we, for they shocked the ancient world by also dissecting living criminals who had been condemned to death. They justified their cruelty in writings, known only through later quotations, to guide surgeons by describing the look of organs while they are still functioning. Before the discovery of anesthetics pain seemed less important than it does now because everybody had to suffer frequent toothaches, at the very least, with nothing but wine to relieve any agony. Also, the Greeks fought particularly shy of corpses, so that a living man strapped to a table may have disquieted them less than the unconfinable ghost of a dead one. Somehow we all dread the power of the dead, even those of us who do not go so far as to believe that Tutankhamen cursed the egyptologists who first broke into his tomb.

From about 275 to 225 B.C. the great Alexandrian anatomists investigated with a freedom that was to disappear for some fifteen hundred years until the Italian Renaissance revived anatomy along with other antique ideas. The Romans had already condemned the dissection of human beings, and rejected it as superfluous because they thought that monkeys were exact and expendable replicas of man. A marble sculpture once believed to come from the Roman house of the physician Musa shows a man's torso opened to expose entrails among which the heart stands upright and central as in the apes. In about A.D. 150–200 the physician Galen, whose writings have survived in greater bulk than those of any other Greek author, described human anatomy at vast length without perhaps ever having dissected a man. At least Vesalius was to accuse him of never having seen a human uterus, even in a dream. But Charles Singer, who studied Galen's text impartially and repeated his dissections of monkeys, says that he described "the soft parts of the ape imposed on the skeleton of man" and might have dissected human beings. This opinion sums up such thorough study that it cannot be bettered.

A picturesque passage in Galen's treatise on anatomical procedure shows how hard it had become to study human anatomy under the Roman Empire: "In Alexandria the doctors demonstrate human bones before your very eyes, so I advise you to go there. But if you cannot go, then study man's bones as I have done, in graves and broken tombs. Once when a river flood washed out a shallow fresh grave, the current swept the corpse 600 feet downstream and beached it in a marshy cove, where I found it with the flesh all rotted away and the bones hanging together (by the gristle) as though an anatomist had prepared it for teaching. Another time, on a roadside hill, I studied a highwayman killed by some travellers whom he had attacked. The local peasantry had refused to bury him, happy to let the birds strip the flesh off his bones in a couple of days, which left his skeleton like a classroom specimen." The Greeks and Romans evidently buried their dead so scrupulously that they left nothing like the bone piles that cluttered every European cemetery in the Middle Ages. Under the Roman Empire the study of anatomy survived in stagnation while immediately "practical" investigations like astronomy, geography, and mechanics held their ground or actually advanced.

The Romans discovered little in medicine because they were so inhibited by practicality that they mistrusted the vagabond and heterodox curiosity that leaps into the dark of the unknown to make the advances that matter. Pliny says in his *Natural History*, XXIX, 8: "Medicine, lucrative though it is, is the only Greek skill that Roman gravity has so far refused to cultivate. Few of our fellow citizens have attempted it, and those who have, have at once deserted to the Greeks. If a doctor prescribes in any language but Greek he loses all credit." Greek imposed on the Romans the mystifying authority that the Latin of medical prescriptions imposes on us.

The Alexandrian anatomists must have had a rough idea of human viscera and a good knowledge of the human skeleton, but how much did they know of human muscles, which might most have helped artists? When Galen wrote his detailed descriptions of muscles, blood vessels, and nerves, how much did he take from now lost Alexandrian writings, and how much did he add out of his own extensive dissection of apes and other animals? These questions are hard to answer, but it seems likely that the Alexandrians concentrated so heavily on the inner organs and the bones that they knew little that could help an artist when carving and painting.

But even if Aristotle and the Alexandrian anatomists had had information useful to artists, they had no effective way of imparting their findings pictorially. Before the invention of printing, an unillustrated text could be published quickly and cheaply in a small edition by dictating to dozens of scribes writing in a room with clear acoustics. But a roomful of copyists could not see a book illustration, let alone reproduce it; and their drawings, no matter how careful, would have degenerated in time through the constant copying that was necessary in public libraries as readers frayed and cracked the brittle papyri. This is why in the first century A.D. the elder Pliny said that he would describe plants, not illustrate them, because words are more accurate than pictures. The impossibility of publishing pictures in many exact facsimiles blocked Greek and Roman descriptive scientists at a certain stage, just as the logical clumsiness of Greek and Roman numerals blocked ancient mathematicians. (Please quickly multiply MXVIII by DCXLIV.)

Yet Greek medicine could not entirely dispense with pictures. Aristotle mentions *schemata* (diagrams) which illustrated two of his lost works. They were probably such rude figures as a

13

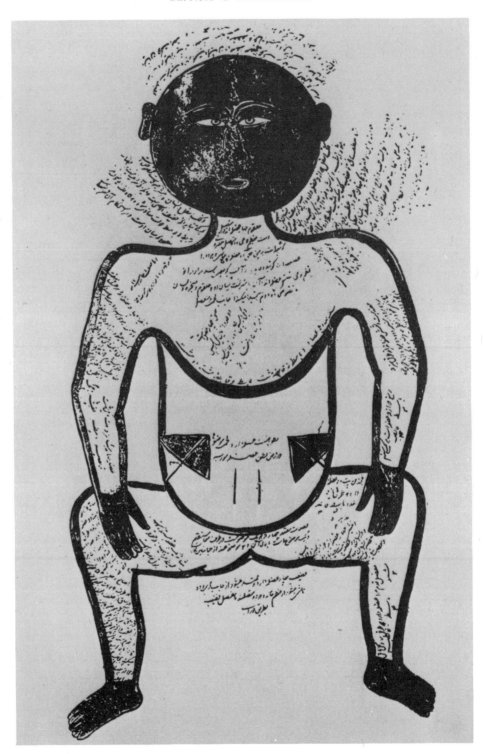

Fig. 7. Muscular system, illustrated in a Persian manuscript, about 1400 A.D.
India Office, London

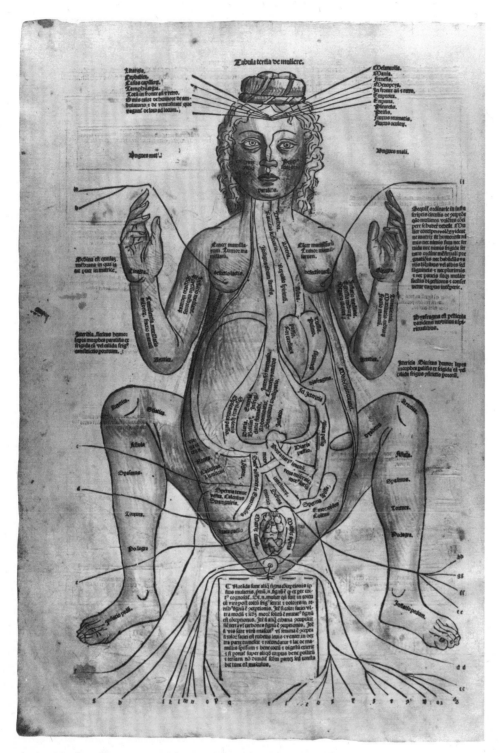

Fig. 8. Woodcut illustration in Johannes de Ketham, *Fasciculus Medicinae*,
Venice (Gregoriis), 1491.
Yale University Medical Library, New Haven

Fig. 9. Byzantine miniature painted in the 10th century A.D. to illustrate
a copy of the *Commentary* by Apollonius of Citium (1st century B.C.).
Biblioteca Laurenziana, Florence

teacher could trace in sand. Little as the Arabs cared for Greek art, they apparently preserved Aristotle's diagrams—certainly deformed by copying—in the sets of five jumping-jack figures that illustrate the bones, muscles, veins, arteries, and nerves in Islamic translations of Greek medical texts from the Middle Ages until after 1800 (fig. 7). The Arabs did not attempt to draw the shape of any muscle or vein, but merely wrote its name in its position inside the outline of the figure. This Arabic (and Greek?) jumping jack appears in Venice in 1491 in a woodcut which represents the uterus so realistically that it must be the first printed picture ever made from an actual dissection (fig. 8). It is odd to see how the Venetian has inserted one of the latest advances of science into a very ancient framework, acting like the Renaissance doctors and geographers who published their epoch-making discoveries as footnotes to Galen or Ptolemy in order to sponsor their innovations with the authority of tradition.

A very different set of Greek medical illustrations came to Europe by a more direct and traceable route. This was a series of illustrations of painful tractions and splints in a Byzantine manuscript on bonesetting, dating about A.D. 900 (fig. 9). These Byzantine illustrations presumably replace some lost original illustrations drawn about 60 B.C. when the treatise was first composed by a Greek bonesetter called Apollonius of Citium. These original illustrations must have had the usual pagan frank delight in athletic nudity, which the Byzantine copyist has censored. This, however, was re-created when the Byzantine pictures were adapted by Francesco Primaticcio about 1540 (fig. 10). Primaticcio's adaptations were in their turn adapted in woodcuts published in Paris in 1544 (fig. 11). Thus for some sixteen hundred years this set of pictures helped men to set bones in spite of reversals of style that changed everything except the basic useful diagram. Each transformation probably looked natural to its contemporaries because, before the rise of Impressionism and Cubism, each generation was so accustomed to the artifices of its own style that it looked at its pictures as if they were windows opening onto nature itself. The average man of the Middle Ages certainly saw nothing unnatural in chaotic perspective, for it is only the exceptional artist who observes innocently enough to transform art into a new harmony with nature.

Ancient papyri of histories, orations, and poems were not illustrated except in rare palace copies because such texts were like musical scores—equipment for performances and not to be admired for themselves. While medical texts were occasionally illustrated, ancient science in general—indeed the whole of the ancient world after Plato—was so hypnotized by logic and the play of words that no scientist knew how to make good use of art, and artists worked apart from writers and scientists because they were nonverbal and semiservile. (If Plato had been a Renaissance Italian, artists like Titian or Michelangelo would have had a word to say in some dialogue or other.) The Renaissance interlude of collaboration between art and science had no parallel before or after, for in antiquity social differences separated artists and scientists even more than specialization does today. Greek and Roman anatomists may never have commissioned sculptors to make models for teaching, unless such be the Vatican's marble viscera, which suggest an anatomical model but could be a

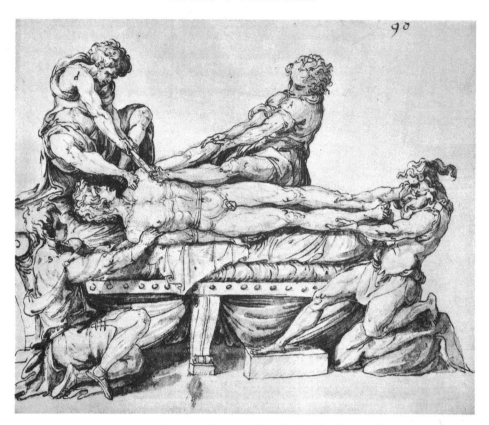

Fig. 10. Francesco Primaticcio (1504–1570). One of the sketches for the woodcut illustrations in Guido Guidi's *Chirurgia* of 1544. Sepia watercolor. Bibliothèque Nationale, Paris

votive offering like the feet, hands, and eyes that ancient convalescents left by thousands at shrines to Aesculapius. The ancient artists' lack of contact with the then available anatomical knowledge shows in the crudeness of their skeletons (fig. 12). Nor could antiquity make anything like the Renaissance muscle men because nobody knew enough about human muscles; antique sculptors had no choice except to show Marsyas before he had been skinned. This has been held to indicate a certain Greek squeamishness, and has been likened to Oedipus blinding himself discretely offstage in Sophocles's tragedy. But the messenger's speech that describes his gory self-mutilation, far from sparing the audience, effectively keys it up for the shock of the last mask of streaming eye sockets—a mask that must have horrified quite as much as any flayed Marsyas. As a general rule, however, Athenians disliked wounds and deformity, and so represented warriors as dying more often than dead. El Greco may have been reverting to his Greek ancestry when he painted martyrdom as an agony of anticipation at the instant when the yet unmutilated body expects the pang.

Fig. 11. Woodcut illustration in Guido Guidi, *Chirurgia*, Paris (Gaultier), 1544.
The Metropolitan Museum of Art, New York.
Harris Brisbane Dick Fund, 1947

Fig. 12. Thracian beaker, between 50 B.C. and 50 A.D.
Staatliche Museen, Preussischer Kulturbesitz,
Antikenmuseum, Berlin

THE GREEK ARTIST AND HIS MODELS

Actually, a Greek artist did not have to know anything about flayed muscles because he could study muscles better in the exercise grounds. The Greek artist who could go every day to a nearby gymnasium to study naked men exercising in sunlight actually gained by not being able to strip the skin from a cadaver in order to learn the full equipment of muscles. Dissection might have confused him by revealing all the muscles at once, while a living athlete kept his art simple and distinct by showing only a few muscles at a time as they bulged one after another to accomplish a series of actions. When a Greek artist watched an arm lift a weight, he saw only those muscles that lift and did not see other muscles that flex only for other actions. Thus the Greeks learned to draw and model with impulsive clarity.

As a Greek artist watched teams of naked men running, boxing, or wrestling, his eye must have gathered a general image from all of them—an image not of John's arm or Henry's arm punching, but a composite image of THE ARM punching, an image that would not exactly be an average of all arms but one composed of those features that struck the artist by their accent. Such a multiple impression would help to explain the generalized character of Greek art, its widely touted ideal beauty, and its inability to make a portrait as Egyptians understood portraits. The everyday accessibility of the gymnasium might also explain why Greek art showed nude men so long before it showed nude women, who rarely undressed in public except at drinking parties in lamplit dimness. When it came to children, Athenians painted and carved many nude boys but practically no nude girls. As worshipers of ripeness and perfection, they may have admired a little boy because he is a complete man in miniature, while rejecting a little girl as an imperfect woman.

While classical Greeks indeed made no portraits as individual as some Egyptian figures, or as specific as the thug heads that Roman sculptors incongruously mounted on generalized Jovian bodies, yet the pediments of Olympia (about 470–460 B.C.) parade the most sharply characterized of all pageants of the growth and aging of man's body as a whole. Starting from the bird-boned, chicken-skinned boys, through the bullet-headed young men with their flat, hard stomachs, on to the blown and sagging elders, each marble actor makes the gesture that exactly sets off his age. While modern physiognomists have read character in the hand, in the profile of the face or the bumps on the skull, the Greeks also read character in the entire man from head to foot. As the Aristotelian *Physiognomics*, III, says: "Hearty eaters are longer from the navel to the chest than from the chest to the throat." Such observations show again how the Greeks scrutinized each other in the gymnasium.

When a modern revivalist like Canova or Flaxman carves an ideal nude in the "Grecian" manner, instead of using Greek art as a springboard for exploration, his figures freeze because he is generalizing from a study of marbles in museums, not from a multiple memory of running, lunging men. Canova constructed nudes as one writes a dead language, by rules of grammar and syntax, while the Greeks worked with a familiarity that often eased into slang.

Since ancient times no artist has been able to watch naked crowds in sunlight so easily as he can on today's bathing beaches. Modern artists profit little by this opportunity because an excursion to a beach is an occasional summer outing, not a daily routine around the corner, and because today's bathers rarely box and wrestle, like the Greeks in their gymnasia, but either sprawl on the sand to absorb the sun, or exercise by swimming, out of sight. Today's abstract artists need the human figure as little as did the decorators of the Alhambra. When artists return to subject matter they also return to a study of the figure, and with it an awareness, at least, of Antique art.

The Greeks took nudity no more casually than we, for they did not go naked naturally, as bushmen do—they undressed. Before they invented the cult of nudity, Odysseus showed how far he was from such freedom when, after losing his clothes by shipwreck, he approached the girls on the beach with a leafy branch held before him. And Pausanias thought it worth recording that, a century or so before the age of classical Greek art, a victorious runner had contrived to let his loincloth slip off while racing at Olympia and so started the fashion for naked contests. Aristophanes said that when a really nice young man sat on the ground in the good old days of decency, he kept his legs stretched flat in front of him, and when he got up he bashfully leveled the hollows that he had pressed into the sand. With such a censorship of prudery to break through, it is no wonder that the Greeks studied the nude with an excitement so intense that Western art still tingles under the impact of their exhibitionism. By contrast, the Japanese made so little of nudity in art because they undress simply for comfort or convenience.

It is odd that at a given moment in history, men should have suddenly chosen to show themselves to the world stripped. Before the classical Greeks, when a man had made himself worth depicting by hunting or fighting or ruling or interceding with the gods, his dignity required clothes. But when a Greek began to fascinate simply by being alive at the peak of his energy, every inch of him became worth an artist's record.

ANATOMY IN GREEK ART

Even though Greek artists seem to have learned nothing from anatomists, they kept pace with Greek physicians in their study of the body. At the moment when Aristotle and his pupils were dissecting, Greek artists revised their basic image of man, so it is worth glancing at the development of anatomy in Greek art.

When we consider Greek art for what it invented for us, we examine it for the epoch-making emergence of the beautiful human being. But a slight shift of interest readjusts any historical event, just as staring at the tiles on the bathroom floor makes the chevrons cluster into hexagons which then run out into diagonals. Each pattern is equally "true." So instead of looking at classical Greek art for what it gave to posterity, it might be interesting to think of it as the epilogue to several thousand years of prehistory. Viewed from the standpoint of progress from its very origins, instead of its consequences, Greek art seems at first sight to split into two unrelated halves—over 2,000 years of prehistoric abstraction disconnected from four or five centuries of naturalistic representation. The squared Cycladic idols, the ancient scratched tree trunks that the Naxians copied in marble, the match-stick men and animals of Attic geometric pottery, all seem to have nothing to do with the sculptures of the Parthenon. Yet actually prehistoric art established a dominant geometry, an architectural vision of the body, which underlay classical art until Aristotle's old age. At about this time, when this basic geometry ceased to inspire fresh inventions, classical art may be said to have ended and Hellenistic art to have begun. This crisis was as acute as the earlier crisis of the sixth and fifth centuries B.C. which created our vision of the nude. A few examples will show the continuity and the break.

Greek styles are easiest to trace in the continuous and datable series of Attic pottery paintings. Since the pots were soon exported, broken, or buried in tombs, their decorators in Athens saw few old ones to influence them, and so drew in current styles with little archaism. Unlike Greek sculpture, Attic vases were not copied or faked in later times because they lay underground out of the reach of Roman collectors. The drawings on Attic pottery must often reflect great Greek paintings the way Florentine woodcuts of the 1490s recall the work of Verrocchio and Botticelli. It is also quite possible that some of the great Greek painters could have begun by decorating pottery, like young Renoir painting roses on china plates, or the seventeenth century Dutch painters who began by engraving on glass. If some of the once-famous Greek paintings had been able to survive a bad climate, we might well think of the Greeks as painters rather than as sculptors. Such is the disaster of December rains.

In an Attic vase painting of the late sixth century B.C., a prehistoric geometry of action dominates the drawing of runners, botching the muscles, scalloping the rib cage, and distorting the

Fig. 13. Panathenaic Prize Amphora. Attic, about 530 B.C. Attributed to the Euphiletos Painter. The Metropolitan Museum of Art, New York. Rogers Fund, 1944

Fig. 14. Red-figure Greek vase by the Douris potter.
British Museum, London

attitude of running more outrageously than in pictures of galloping horses before the speed photograph (fig. 13). Any painter who ever ran two steps must have known that you cannot advance your left leg while advancing your left arm, but this seemingly intentional awkwardness makes a pattern that fairly sweats with the charge of burly men hustling to shove past each other. Traditional schemes and proportions were still putting blinders on the observing eye almost as much as they had done in geometric art. In about 490 B.C., a later painter like Douris (fig. 14) has limbered up the old geometry in an outline of such sensitive tension that it almost alone suggests the entire inner modeling. An ancient abstract tradition, an intimacy with the body, and a command of drawing all balanced in Douris with such liveliness that he could throw out a lariat of contour as exactly as Matisse at his best. But nearly a century later, in 340–339 B.C., the artist no longer has a memory of geometric tradition to organize what he sees, leaving the painter with no scheme into which to fit an embarrassing multiplicity of muscles. Once the painter has lost his inherited rules of thumb, he is boggled by the inexhaustible complexity of the body. This characterizes one great half (the experimental half) of Hellenistic art.

Greek sculpture develops more complicatedly than pottery because statues are harder to ship than jugs and cups, forcing some sculptors to travel to where their work was needed and so to confuse local styles. And unlike pottery, ancient statues survived aboveground to be collected, adapted, copied, and faked, thus eventually separating sculptors into revivalists working for the antique market, and experimentalists. Nevertheless, the memory of a geometric tradition ceased to inspire at about the same time in sculpture as in the drawings on pottery.

When the very ancient solid geometry of Greek prehistoric sculpture first showed signs of beginning to break up, the fission generated energy, which a breakup does in the world of the imagination as violently as in the world of physics. In a sudden century Greek statues stepped forth from their primitive tree-trunk stiffness in order to walk, to run, to box, and then to relax into every casual attitude, while bones and muscles developed their complex interplay. The first monumental sculptures in the round of men in action set an example that still haunts our art.

The crack-up of abstract rigidity startles so much that anatomy at first seems also to have left abstract schemes. But in reality prehistoric Greek sculpture, while not as sophisticated or as imaginative as African sculpture, nevertheless managed to impose a cubism so basic that its elegance of proportion, its sense of blocked-out grandeur, continued to guide artists right into the classical age (fig. 15). Polycleitus, who worked from 460 to 420 B.C., said that his figures made their effect through adjustments of proportion—he did not say through imitation of nature. And indeed, he organized the chest and belly of his figures into a rhythm of bumps and hollows which boldly emphasize or suppress actual features in order to create a pattern that carries at a distance like the exaggerations of an actor's mask (fig. 16). He remodeled nature especially where the legs and arms join the trunk in order to weld four spindly shapes onto the central solid. In contriving transitions to unite elements of a smaller to a larger scale, Polycleitus was as adroit as the Greek architects when

Fig. 15. Statuette of Apollo. Bronze, about 700 B.C.
Museum of Fine Arts, Boston. Francis Bartlett Collection

they developed varieties of capitals to blend slender columns with a massive architrave, and so to make harmony supply the place of invention in the unimaginative stone carpentry that they inherited from their wooden prehistory. The Greeks acknowledged the common purpose of these devices when they compared man's body to architecture in a simile to which the Renaissance paid at least lip service.

Polycleitus's conscious and authoritarian grandeur of design packed such brutality into his reinforced concrete torsos that they stay alive even in the marble copies through which we must guess at his lost bronze originals. Less than a century later, the prehistoric dominance of design finally died away, leaving Praxiteles (about 370–330 B.C.) to turn flabby in the dozens of reproductions made after his once admired lost works. What many consider to be his one surviving original, the Hermes (fig. 17) shows why. This body is not an abstract composition. It is *the* body, all warmth and heartbeat enticing the hand to explore the skin, the muscles, the bones in all their varying resistance. Who could ever copy so personal a sensuality? A copyist could transmit nothing but the scattered languor of the pose and the jarring disparity of the dinky baby floating somewhere in front of the grown man—a clash of scale and axis that recurs in the Acropolis at Athens, where the dainty shrine of Wingless Victory has perched askew on the left arm, as it were, of the wide and deep Propylea. Praxiteles developed naturalness of anatomy at the expense of the traditional grand design. His Hermes is no longer the hunting animal simplified by abstract articulations flowing into one lunge of action, for the effect of life no longer comes from clarity of structure and movement but from abundance and exactitude of anatomical detail. One can hardly believe that such a master of surface anatomy almost certainly could not draw a rib cage or even a shinbone.

Praxiteles could not have examined the body inch by inch solely by watching groups of men in the gymnasium. One would think that he could have studied anatomy in such detail only through dissection, which did not exist generally. What then might have made the fourth-century change that divides classical from Hellenistic art?

The answer could lie in a chance remark of Pliny's, XXXV, 153, where he says that Lysippus's brother Lysistratos in about 325 B.C. "was the first to reproduce the human form by molding plaster on the body itself, then pouring wax into the plaster mold and retouching [the wax cast]. He was the first to get exact likenesses instead of beautifying." (*Hominis autem imaginem gypso e facie ipsa primus omnium expressit, ceraque in eam formam gypsi infusa emendare instituit.*) Bronze statues could be cast directly from retouched life casts, as Rodin was accused of doing when he exhibited his *Age of Bronze* in 1877.

Pliny's date is probably over a century too late, for Dietrich von Bothmer has pointed out to me that the hand and feet of the bronze Charioteer of Delphi (480–470 B.C.) look like retouched life casts (fig. 18). Indeed their exact and complex articulation contrasts sharply with the spherical abstraction of the face, which would have been harder to cast from life. The arm and hand are much too dainty to go with the rest of the statue, which reminds one of Bernini's saying that a sculptor

Fig. 16. Doryphorus (Spear Bearer). Roman copy after an original of about 450–440 B.C.
by Polycleitus. Marble. National Museum, Naples
Alinari/Art Resource, Inc.

Fig. 17. Hermes, by Praxiteles. About 330 B.C. (or copy?). Marble.
Museum, Olympia
Alinari/Art Resource, Inc.

Fig. 18. Charioteer, from the Sanctuary of Apollo at Delphi.
Bronze, about 470 B.C. Museum, Delphi
Alinari/Art Resource, Inc.

must exaggerate the size of a projecting arm and hand because "the air gnaws at it." Since almost all early big bronzes have been melted down, one cannot tell how many may have incorporated life casts. The Zeus or Poseidon from Artemesion is over life-size and shows nothing like life casting.

Can Pliny have meant that Lysistratos was the first sculptor to study life casts besides merely using them for assemblages? What a pity it is that we have to guess at so much ancient technology through casual asides by a magpie compiler of texts like Pliny and a Herr Baedecker like Pausanias, who probably never faced the heat, dirt, and banging of a foundry, and certainly knew nothing of the arts from practicing them.

Pliny also says that Lysistratos invented casting from statues. If these two kinds of casts from living bodies and from statues really came into general use in the age of Praxiteles, they might help to explain why Hellenistic sculpture split into experimental naturalism, studied from life casts, and the revival of past styles and downright reproduction of antiques, based on casts from old statues. The revivalists who worked in retrospective styles were epigones like the contemporary profession of editors of classical texts. Both arose when Greeks felt dislocated in the new loneliness of the polyglot commercial seaports, and so clung to the memory of the vanished solidarity of the clan and the lost snugness of the city-state. The retrospective academicism of Hellenistic art was ultimately to triumph in the passionate formality of Byzantium, just as the discipline of Hellenistic textual criticism flowered in Byzantine theology.

Roman collectors could buy marble reproductions of famous statues made with completely accurate proportions. These antique copies always simplified the modeling because they were not, like most modern copies, bronzes cast directly from plasters that in their turn were directly cast on the originals. Instead, the ancient copyists reproduced old marbles and bronzes in new marbles by using a triangular frame as a simple pointing machine. Even when they chiseled down the new marble in points set very close together, they still missed details of transition between the points. What was kept and what was lost shows clearly in a modern plaster cast of the great, though weathered fifth-century relief of Demeter, Persephone, and Triptolemus from Eleusis, into which the Metropolitan Museum has inlaid almost exactly fitting marble fragments of an antique copy (figs. 19, 20). This remarkable survival of a classical Greek masterpiece and an ancient full-size copy shows how the original Attic sculptor, looking at a living boy, carved very differently from the copyist, who was working a pointing machine on a plaster cast of the original. The original has delicacies of transition, trembling irregularities and surprises of modeling that the pointing machine has smoothed out in a broad, clear scheme. The original pleases us more because it is unexpected and alive, but the impersonal simplification of the copy teaches a lesson that is easier to learn. So it is probably lucky that the Renaissance artists found more Roman copies than Greek originals when they were studying to re-create an art of the nude in action, because the copies gave them an intelligible scheme into which they could fit the muscles that the dissector's knife was by then discovering.

The Cycladic beginning and the Hellenistic ending of Greek sculpture both abound in nude

Fig. 19. Demeter, Triptolemos, and Persephone. Fragmentary marble relief. Roman copy of
a Greek work of about 450–440 B.C. Missing portions restored with a cast of the Greek original.
The Metropolitan Museum of Art, New York. Rogers Fund, 1914

Fig. 20. Demeter, Triptolemos, and Persephone. Eleusinian marble relief, Greek, about 450–440 B.C. National Museum, Athens

statues of women, but the intervening brief high classical age produced few. In that middle time the Greeks set such store by clarity that several of their writers praised a man's evident muscle and bone above a woman's more enveloped modeling. As an anonymous follower of Aristotle put it in his *Physiognomy*: "A woman has a smaller head, a narrower face, a more slender neck, a weaker chest and smaller ribs than a man, as well as loins and thighs more padded with flesh. She has knock knees, spindly calves, neat feet, weak muscles and softer moister flesh, so that her whole body charms instead of imposing. Men are in every way the opposite, for their whole nature is more brave and honest, while women are more cowardly and dishonest." We will see such comparisons revived in the Renaissance.

Antique marble copies achieved a crystallized grandeur of design that has made them ideal patterns for teaching the construction of the figure. The anatomy of this sculpture is classic because it is inescapable. Now and then the West has rebelled against its supercilious Greek tutors, but we can never expel them permanently from our imagination. The Greeks persist in our art because they were the first to draw and carve man's body in all its play of action. They persist in our literature and our psychology because they were the first to explore man's emotions in much of their range and depth.

Graeca capta ferum victorem cepit, et artes intulit agresti Latio.

THE ARABS

AFTER Greek art went underground during the Middle Ages, Greek science survived among the Arabs. From about A.D. 850 to 950 the Califs of Bagdad had careful translations made of the main Greek books on mathematics, botany, and medicine. The Arabs did not think of the Greeks as artists and poets, as we do, but as inventors, engineers, and physicians. The Arab Al Jahiz wrote that "the ancient Greeks taught others how to make things, but did not themselves make them." Arabic poetry seems unaware of Greek poetry, and Islamic art is unaware of classical Greek art.

The Arabs who translated the anatomy of Aristotle and Galen became better physicians than the Europeans who forgot it. Yet Arabs added nothing to Greek anatomy because they accepted the Koran, and to a lesser extent any book, without questioning, and because they dreaded dissecting human beings even more than the Greeks did. Koranic tradition forbids a Muslim to cut into a dead man "even though he may have swallowed a priceless pearl." Arab medical students were finally allowed to dissect Jews and Christians in 1836, but to this day Muslims may riot at the mere rumor of a legal autopsy to determine suspected murder. After the great age of Bagdad had showed a much livelier and more varied curiosity than contemporary Europe, the Arab promise failed. As President

Ayub Khan eloquently said in Cairo in November 1960: "The kingdoms and crowns which the Muslims have lost in the course of history matter far less than the kingdom of the free and searching mind which they have lost in the process of intellectual stagnation."

Nowadays we no longer need Arabic translations of Greek medical texts because we have recovered many of the Greek originals. But the Arabs did us a service by copying the Greek anatomical diagrams which have disappeared from Western manuscripts (fig. 7). They preserved these diagrams as aids to the written tradition which they may have valued even more highly than original experiment.

THE MEDIAEVAL CHURCH

Now that we come to anatomy in the Christian world, it is important to correct the popular misconception that the Church officially discountenanced dissection. The error probably arose because, on September 27, 1299, Pope Boniface VIII threatened to excommunicate those who "moved by a kind of impious piety, savagely hack a dead body limb from limb, cook it in water and strip the flesh off the skeleton in order to send the bones where the dead person had asked to be buried." This was often done to travelers who died abroad wishing to be shipped home for burial. As one instance among many, St. Louis was stewed in wine under the walls of Carthage, his flesh buried there and his bones in St. Denis. Boniface VIII promulgated his edict a few months before the great jubilee year of 1300 was about to crowd Rome with hordes of pilgrims, many of whom were sure to die begging for burial at home.

What made the Pope so vehement against this "German custom"? The boiling could not have seemed particularly gruesome in an age when executions bloodied every city square, nor particularly unsanitary while every graveyard stank with remains in plain sight. The Pope undoubtedly wished to prevent the confusion of reassembling disjointed bodies at the busy day of last judgment, a provision implied by ecclesiastical licenses for dissection when they stipulated that all parts must be kept for burial together. In early Christian times when scoffers asked how the Resurrection was to disentangle cannibals from their dinners, St. Augustine attempted an answer in the last book of his *City of God*: "God will restore eaten flesh to the man in whom it first became human flesh, for it is a loan taken by the famished cannibal and, like any borrowed goods, must be returned to the lender. Of course the flesh of the famished cannibal will be replenished by Him Who can recall even fumes from the air." St. Thomas Aquinas restated this in proper legal language at the end of his *Summa*, half a century before Pope Boniface's decree.

John Donne played with the old question when he asked: "Where be all the splinters of that Bone, which a Shot hath shivered and scattered in the Ayre?... What cohaerance, what sympathy, what dependence maintaines any relation, any correspondance, between that arm that was lost in Europe, and that legge that was lost in Afrique or Asia, scores of yeers between?"

The decree of 1299 recommended, instead of boiling, "burial near the place of death until the bones shall be bare enough to send to the requested tomb." Since the decree did not state that this was to prevent dispersing the body, it read like a decree against maceration in general. Therefore, seventeen years later, the anatomist Mondino wrote that he would not describe maceration "propter peccatum," although he freely described all other aspects of dissection. In 1354 the anatomist Guido da Vegevano was probably still misinterpreting the decree of 1299 when he wrote "the church forbids dissecting human bodies, so I will demonstrate dissection by representations (*figuras*)."

The Church not only never declared itself officially against properly conducted dissection, but often actually fostered it. When Leonardo in Rome complained that an unidentified artisan "hindered me from dissecting, blaming it before the Pope and at the hospital," he did not indicate any Church policy against anatomy, since he had dissected freely in Florence at the ecclesiastical hospital of Santa Maria Nuova. Michelangelo, when he was about seventeen, was commissioned to carve a wooden crucifix (now lost) for the high altar of Santo Spirito in Florence. The prior of Santo Spirito helped him to study for the crucified Christ by giving him cadavers from the monastery hospital to dissect in the monastery itself. In January 1508, the son of the Florentine apothecary Luca Landucci stood in a crowd to watch a dissection in the monastery of Santa Croce. In Holland the first dissection took place about 1550 in a nunnery. As late as the 1760s when Houdon modeled his celebrated muscle man, he did so from anatomy classes held for French Academy students in the church of San Luigi de' Francesi in Rome. These random instances show how usual it was to dissect under ecclesiastical auspices.

The papacy helped directly when the University of Tübingen asked Pope Sixtus IV for "permission to take bodies of legally executed criminals from the place of execution and to dissect them according to medical rules and practice without any dispensation or special license from the Holy See." Sixtus IV, who had studied at Bologna when it was the world's center of medical research, granted the request in April 1482 "provided the dissected bodies be given burial." The five year old university probably needed the Pope to defend it against the city fathers of Tübingen, for civil governments hindered anatomy in Germany as late as the eighteenth century.

Ten years later the university statutes of Tübingen laid down the rules for anatomy lessons. (Similar but usually simpler regulations prevailed elsewhere.) "We ordain that every four years or oftener the body of an executed criminal shall be anatomized during the coldest weather about Christmas. All who wish to see the anatomy must attend and pay for an early morning mass for the dead, and must devoutly intercede for the soul of the dead. This done, the professor shall take his fellows and pupils to the place where the anatomy is to be held, shall call them to order and shall read from the writings of the doctors, especially Mondino, about the part of the body to be demonstrated. After discussion, each organ shall be shown plainly for inspection. When the anatomy is completed, the body with all its organs shall be carried to the grave accompanied by the doctors of medicine and the masters and scholars of the faculty of arts." Some of these regulations were probably disregarded, for five years later the university added this bylaw: "We ordain that the faculty of medicine cause a chest to be made, with a lock and key, in which to shut up the fragments and remains of the body being anatomized, as well as the instruments used, until the time of burial." This insured the carrying out of the Pope's injunctions to the letter.

ITALY

ITALY had a breadth of mind that was to allow man to dissect more regularly and more systematically than the Greeks had done in their Alexandrian heyday. Throughout the Middle Ages the Italians never quite forgot that antiquity had accepted everything human. So when Renaissance men set out to do all that they read about in Greek and Latin books, they did not forget dissection. At least the idea of modern anatomy existed in the freethinking, cosmopolitan south of Italy in about 1241, when the Emperor Frederick II forbade any surgeon to practice "unless he had studied the anatomy of human bodies in the schools for at least a year." Though the students may have studied nothing but diagrams like those in Islamic manuscripts (fig. 7) instead of actually dissecting, the edict at least foreshadows modern state regulations for medical degrees.

The systematic teaching of anatomy by dissection began in the late 1200s at the University of Bologna, where the powerful law schools probably prepared the way by ordering autopsies to investigate possible murders. By 1316 courses in anatomy had become so usual that an Italian doctor, Mondino (Raimondo de' Luzzi), wrote the first classroom manual, a mere inventory that wastes no time on descriptions. It begins: "Lay the beheaded or hanged body on a trestle"—and then itemizes man in the order of his decay: belly, thorax, head, and extremities, each section to be completed in one day. In such haste students could check the finding list, but could hardly examine each part individually. Yet for all Mondino's shortcomings, his list was so practical that it guided Leonardo da Vinci and survived the appearance of Vesalius's great anatomy to persist in some classrooms until after 1600, when his homely mediaeval Latin began to embarrass professors who prefered Vesalius's erudite and allusive turn of phrase, or else read Galen in the original Greek.

Mondino wrote as though he had dissected with his own hands while explaining to his students, but when his text came to be printed in Venice in the 1490s the various editions were illustrated with a woodcut that shows how classroom practice had changed in 175 years (fig. 21). In this illustration a lecturer in a high pulpit (*cathedra*) reads from a book while an assistant with a pointer (*ostensor*) indicates to a barber-surgeon (*demonstrator*) where to strike the cadaver with a cleaver. The spectators in the woodcut do not care to explore but to memorize a standard text like any medical students today. The barber-surgeon knows that if he should find anything that is not in the lecturer's book he had better slip it quietly into the scrapbasket lest he ruffle the authority of the schools by intruding crudities of fact. Such a lecturer acquired no practical experience in dissecting, while the barber-surgeon developed a butcher's ignorant dexterity in chopping joints and extracting organs without discovering their connections or functions. Each was only half of a true anatomist.

Vesalius was later to ridicule this sterile dissociation of the lecturer droning by rote high above the barber-surgeon's chopping. During the Middle Ages the barber-surgeon remained a menial unfit to wear a doctor's robes, as the Venetian woodcut shows him, because his patients usually died of blood poisoning after his messy cutting, whereas the physician rose higher because his patients often managed to survive the potions that he prescribed from reading his Greek and Latin books.

The lecturer in the Venetian woodcut looks like a preacher in the pulpit or a judge on the bench because he actually partakes of both. As the spectators watch the criminal's body disintegrate they see punishment continuing beyond the gallows in a sort of morality play. To point this dramatic moral, the anatomy theater at Leyden displayed a copy of Michelangelo's Last Judgment.

The first anatomical demonstrations, like the earliest English plays, were probably staged in courtyards, as one may see in the frontispiece of Vesalius's *Fabrica* of 1543 (fig. 22). Why did Vesalius show an old-fashioned courtyard instead of Padua's pioneer oval anatomical theater where he had taught, and which he may have helped to build three years before? As a humanist snob, was he ashamed of a building that must then have seemed as raw as a garage today? Certainly the classical colonnade of his frontispiece makes a fitting preface to the mythological allusions of his prose and the antique allure of his illustrations, but it is a pity that he could not have given us a contemporary picture of a fascinating experimental building.

By 1500 the Christian drama of anatomy had begun to attract such a public that there was at least the plan of putting up temporary anatomical theaters "in the round." Soon many universities were building actual theaters—Padua leading in 1540, then Montpellier in 1556, Leyden in 1594, Bologna in 1595, Basel in 1599, and so on everywhere except in Eastern Europe and perhaps England. These were theaters in every sense, selling tickets for front row or balcony, and sticking up posters to advertise performances that began right after the hanging or beheading of a criminal. The victim had to be from out of town except at the Medici university of Pisa which allowed doctors and medical students to dissect anybody—even each other—if the family consented. Fallopius says that Pisa cooperated to the extent of sometimes poisoning a criminal with opium instead of hanging or beheading him so as to supply the anatomist with unmangled material.

Anatomical demonstrations usually occurred during Carnival when the weather was still cold enough to preserve a cadaver, and the festive season furnished an audience of masqueraders and

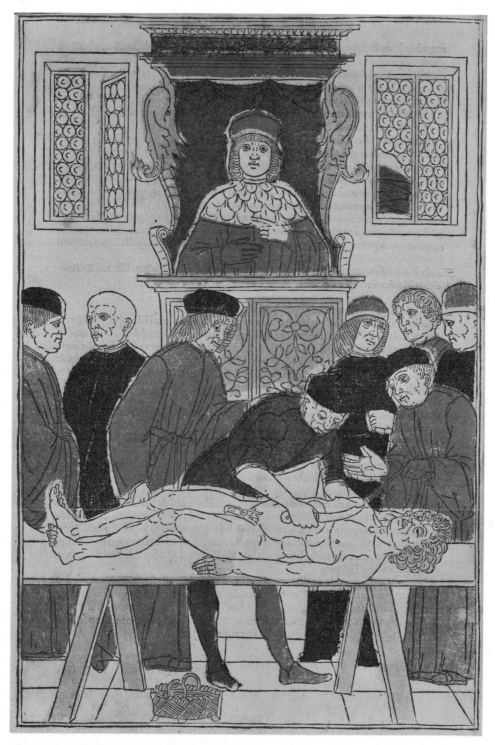

Fig. 21. Stencil-colored woodcut illustrating Mondino's treatise in Johannes de Ketham,
Fascicolo di Medicina, Venice (Gregoriis), 1493/94.
The Metropolitan Museum of Art, New York. Harris Brisbane Dick Fund, 1938

Fig. 22. Woodcut after John Stephen of Calcar in Andreas Vesalius,
De Humani corporis fabrica, Basel (Oporinus), 1555.
The Metropolitan Museum of Art, New York.
Gift of Dr. Alfred E. Cohn, in honor of William M. Ivins, Jr., 1953

women of the town who would pay a penny or two to drop in for a look between other sideshows. The city council of Leyden proposed the playing of flutes to attract a larger public. Even in the daytime the dissections often took place by candlelight. In the still extant theater at Padua eight candles burned in two chandeliers, while another eight moved where needed in the hands of students. Nowadays color movies often replace anatomical theaters because they can show more detail to more students. The theatricality of anatomical demonstrations is learnedly and ingeniously explored in William Heckscher's book, *Rembrandt's Anatomy of Dr. Tulp.*

The anatomies must have disturbed the midwinter routine of university life, for the Medici Archives (filza 1174, carta 4) contains a letter from a student at Pisa called Jacopo Dani, who wrote on January 5, 1548/9: "The students are still attending the anatomical demonstrations, which ought to end soon, after which the students of liberal arts can resume their lectures, which this anatomist interrupts every year. However, law lectures continue." *Quest' Anatomista* must have been Fallopius, who was then starting to teach at Pisa. In 1538 Etienne Dolet published a Latin poem describing the sensation that Rabelais made with a demonstration at Lyons. The corpse glories in being rescued from his restless swinging on the gallows in order to serve for demonstrating the Creator's masterpiece to a vast surrounding audience.

In 1502 the anatomist Alessandro Benedetti published specifications for an ideal temporary theater, which were followed in many permanent theaters. "Temporary theaters should be built in large and well-aired places, with seats in circles as in the Colosseum in Rome and the arena at Verona. They must be big enough to accommodate many spectators without crowding the teacher. There should be two ushers to expel intruders and two honest doormen to collect entrance fees to pay for the instruments. Lay the cadaver on a high table in the middle where the teacher can reach it easily."

MEDIAEVAL ARTISTS

D ISSECTION and artistic anatomy evolved at the same pace in the Middle Ages as they had in ancient Greece. The artistic evolution shows most clearly in the torsos of Christ on the Cross, because this is the one nude figure that every Christian artist had to cope with sooner or later. In one of the earliest Crucifixions, a fifth century ivory in the British Museum (fig. 23), Christ, young, deep-chested and robustly muscled, extends his arms like a heavyweight champion who has thrown down his challenge to the world. This marks the end of antiquity rather than the start of Christian art, for the bull-throated athlete of the antique arena never mounted the Cross again except briefly when Rubens painted him out of his deep archaeological studies.

Fig. 23. Crucifixion. Ivory, 5th century. British Museum, London

Fig. 24. Crucifix. Spanish, second half of the 12th century.
The Metropolitan Museum of Art, New York.
The Cloisters Collection, Samuel D. Lee Fund, 1935

43

Fig. 25. Crucifixion, drawn by Villard de Honnecourt, about 1240.
Bibliothèque Nationale, Paris

Fig. 26. Giotto. Crucifixion. Fresco, between 1303–13. Scrovegni Chapel, Padua
SCALA/Art Resource, Inc.

Fig. 27. Jan van Eyck. Adam and Eve, from the Ghent Altarpiece in the
Vijd Chapel in St. Bavo's Cathedral, Ghent. 1426–1432
SCALA/Art Resource, Inc.

Mediaeval spirituality quickly volatilized the antique boxer into a diagram, an insubstantial skein that remained standard for almost a thousand years (fig. 24). Yet many mediaeval artists must have been aware of the antique even when it hardly shows in their style, for Villard de Honnecourt in about 1250 was sketching ancient sculptures as eagerly, though not as accurately, as any Renaissance Italian, and he caught a little of the muscular breadth of the antique in his Crucifixion (fig. 25). Half a century later Giotto evidently studied his various Crucifixions from life (fig. 26). He probably traveled near public dissections, but if he ever attended any, he did not observe enough internal structure to pull together the vague superficial indications of his torsos. And indeed, why should he have bothered to study the organization of a rib cage when he almost always painted it swathed under a woolen cloak? Yet Giotto's glance in the direction of the living nude set a course for Italian art, just as he provided a classic model for the future by the simple bulk of his forms, the geometric interlocking of his figures, and the drive of his dramatic urgency.

Mediaeval artists drew summary, insufficient nudes in spite of seeing people without clothes in community baths and in their own beds because they thought that human nakedness merely proved man's fallen estate, God having decked even the animals with fur and feathers. The nudity which shamed our first parents as soon as they realized that they had sinned was also one of the most pathetic of the humiliations undergone by Christ on the Cross.

The Middle Ages concentrated a pitiless scrutiny in Jan van Eyck's Adam and Eve on the Ghent Altar, painted before 1432 (fig. 27). Van Eyck probably knew as little of dissection as any early Greek, but he also observed as sharply as any Greek. Yet because he did not live among nudes in action as the Greeks did, he could not imagine the body as muscled for moving. So his Eve is merely pneumatic, and his Adam falls apart into those random details that caught his attention as he painted directly from a particular man fixed in a glare striking indoors from the summer sunlight outside the window. It is the unrelated particularity of details like the hip, elbow, and collar bones that makes Van Eyck's Adam not nude but naked. In 1784, when classicism began to revive the generalized nude, Adam looked so indecently portraitlike that he and Eve had to be removed from the altar and locked in a closet for almost eighty years.

45

THE RENAISSANCE

MEDIAEVAL artists had few nudes to paint or carve—Adam and Eve with the apple, St. Sebastian bound, Christ being baptized, nailed to the Cross, or dead—all passive figures that stand or lie down. But Italian artists suddenly ran into more strenuous problems in the early 1400s when the new enthusiasm for Greek and Latin literature demanded pictures for stories in Ovid, Virgil, and Plutarch. Ancient copyists had transmitted the words but had rarely reproduced whatever pictures must have decorated at least a few antique palace scrolls. Yet a revival of Greek and Roman subjects in art obviously called for nudes, as anyone could see from the antique marbles and painted vases that spade and plough struck everywhere in Italy. So for the first time in more than a thousand years, artists were asked to draw nudes moving with the energy of gods and heroes. Nudity no longer exposed man's debasement but adorned him more handsomely than brocade. Since artists could not study these Greek problems as the Greeks had done—in the gymnasium— they were driven to learn from the dissections that had been more or less public for a century.

The artists' changing attitude toward anatomy evolved rapidly in the Italian writings on art. The first Italian treatise on painting, written by Cennino Cennini about 1400 in the north of Italy, never mentions drawing from life and dismisses all anatomy by saying jauntily: "I will acquaint you with the proportions of a man. I omit those of a woman because not one of them is perfectly proportioned. A man's left side has one rib less than a woman's, and throughout his body there are bones. The handsome man is dark, the woman blond." One assumes that artists must always have studied living models, as they do today, but did they? When did the Greeks begin? Some questions are worth asking even though there is no answer.

A mere generation after Cennini, Leon Battista Alberti analyzed figure drawing as a problem in proportion and construction. "To get the right proportions in painting living creatures, first visualize their bony insides, for bones, being rigid, establish fixed measurements. Then attach tendons and muscles in their places and finally clothe the bones and muscles with flesh and skin. You may object that, as I said elsewhere, a painter has no concern with what he cannot see. So be it, but if to paint dressed figures you must first draw them nude and then dress them, so to paint nudes you must first situate the bones and muscles before you cover them with flesh and skin in order to show clearly where the muscles are."

Although Alberti does not mention dissection, it was then the only way for a painter to get a working knowledge of the skeleton and muscles because anatomical drawings in medical treatises (to judge by those that survive) were little better than the mediaeval and Islamic diagrams. Alberti's procedure in building up the figure by wrapping the skeleton in muscles, flesh, and finally clothes was to become standard practice in Italy and then in the whole Western world. He was not only

Fig. 28. Lorenzo Ghiberti. Noah, from the bronze doors of the Baptistry, Florence. 1425–1452.
Alinari/Art Resource, Inc.

the first to state what was to become an axiom of art but he also, half a century before Leonardo, thought of the body as a mechanism functioning by layers. Alberti could hardly have invented this revolutionary way of analyzing the body out of his own artistic practice, which was mostly architectural. He must have derived his writings on anatomy, even more than those on perspective, from talks with some intellectual painter like Piero della Francesca, though Piero's surviving writings treat the body as a problem in perspective.

The first artist ever to mention dissection seems to be Lorenzo Ghiberti, who died in 1455. He says in the second book of his *Commentaries* that a sculptor must have watched dissections (*haver veduto notomia*) to know the bones, muscles, tendons, and ligaments in order to compose the statue of a man. After quoting Avicenna's list of bones he burst out: "O most noble! Without knowing the bones in the human body no one can shape a manly statue." It strikes us today as odd that Ghiberti should not refer to a woman's statue, and seems never to have made an important one—not even a Madonna—but his wide acquaintance with antique literature probably persuaded him that man was the fairer creature. He mentions dissection so casually that public anatomies must have been common in Florence before 1450.

Ghiberti shows no results of dissection in his early sculpture in the international Gothic style, where he skimmed over anatomy in his sinuously floating figures. But after about 1420 he changed, when his study of antique sculpture showed itself in more athletic action, heavier bone and broader muscle. In at least one figure—the drunken Noah in the second Baptistry doors (fig. 28)—he modeled a shin with tendons that show plainly only in dissection. This figure, probably made in the early 1430s, might be the first into which an artist put structure that does not appear in a living body, but must be discovered by cutting into a dead one. In the 1420s dissection may have done as much as the antique to mature Ghiberti's style.

ITALIAN ARTISTS AS DISSECTORS

RENAISSANCE ambitions to become a universal man produced the first great artists who also dissected. The time for universality had actually already gone by when a man could realize Bacon's ambition "I take all knowledge to my province," for the last man whose head contained all the important information of his age was probably Dante (1265–1321), although omniscience such as his stood as a target to aim at until at least the age of Leibniz (1646–1716) long after modern specialization had established itself. Once the Renaissance artists started dissecting, they quickly discovered more than the doctors ever had about the look and functioning of the bones and muscles. They hardly bothered with the viscera, which could not help them to draw the figure and which had been the physicians' first consideration when investigating the seats of illness.

Artists saw what doctors had not seen because they approached anatomy with an entirely different practical purpose and because you do not really see a thing until you try to draw it, no matter how amateurishly. Lynn Thorndyke has aptly observed in his *History of Science* that in the Renaissance "sculpture and painting were more exact and interesting pursuits than physics and chemistry."

By the mid-1500s dissections had become every Florentine artist's routine. In a draft of a letter by Baccio Bandinelli in the Biblioteca Nazionale (filza 2, no.10,c.4), the sculptor writes to an unnamed duke: "I will show you that I know how to dissect the brain, and also living men, as I have dissected dead ones to learn my art." The undated draft does not identify the duke, but it bears out Michelangelo's remark that Bandinelli was brutal as a sculptor and brutal as a man. His boastful offer to vivisect must have been more for advertising than for practice, intending to catch a patron who was curious about the horrified Roman reports of Alexandrian vivisections.

Another casual reference to dissection came from Giorgio Vasari in 1528 when, at the age of seventeen, he went home to Arezzo to paint his first important picture, the *Deposition*, which still hangs there in the Annunziata. About February he wrote to Michelangelo's friend, the Florentine physician Bartolommeo Rontini: "When you come I would be grateful if you would bring that book of the bones and dissections which I gave you last year, because I need it, not having access to

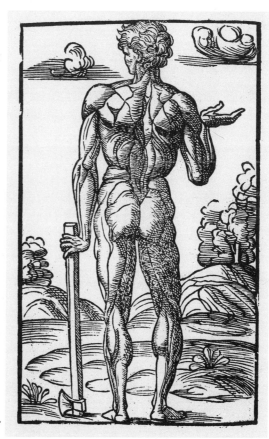

Fig. 29. Woodcut illustration in Berengario da Carpi, *Commentaria . . . super anatomia Mundini*, Bologna (Benedictis), 1521. New York Academy of Medicine Library

cadavers here as I have in Florence." The long established Florentine practice of dissection had evidently not spread to the provinces. Vasari must have felt that he needed to demonstrate anatomical knowledge because he was painting from a design by Rosso, who had dissected enough to prepare an anatomy book for publication.

What sort of an anatomical book had Vasari given to the doctor? In print, the only adequate pictures of bones and muscles were the woodcuts that Berengario da Carpi had published in Bologna five to seven years earlier. But Berengario's skeletons are too wrong to help a painter, and his muscle men (fig. 29) are hardly better. Vasari probably meant some notebook that he himself had drawn from dissections or had copied from one of the many Florentine artists who must have made hundreds of working drawings of anatomy—useful unhandsome notations that would hardly have seemed worth preserving fifteen years after Vasari's letter, when Vesalius published the detailed dramatic woodcuts that artists have referred to ever since.

The precursor of these many Florentine artist anatomists was Antonio Pollaiuolo (1432–1498) who ran the most varied and enterprising artistic workshop in Florence. Vasari says that "he understood the nude in a more modern way than the masters before him. He skinned many human bodies to study the anatomy and was the first who thus investigated the action of the muscles in order to draw them correctly. Antonio engraved on copper a combat of these nude male figures." This print, known as "The Battle of the Ten Naked Men," may have been engraved as early as the 1460s (fig. 30). It was probably the first really large and elaborate engraving, and was certainly the first printed repertory of the muscles. Its publication made history because it crammed a whole course of figure drawing into one picture by assembling bodies stooping, reaching, striding and striking, and crowded each body with all its muscles quite regardless of which would flex for these actions and which would not. These figures are too active to represent dissected cadavers, and yet they look a good deal less than naked. If not flayed, their skin must be transparent to reveal all the muscles and sinews that Pollaiuolo huddled in higgledy-piggledy. Leonardo da Vinci was probably thinking of this celebrated engraving, or at least of Pollaiuolo's work in general, when he wrote that a good painter must know which muscles work for any given action "and must emphasize the bulging of those muscles only and not of the rest, as some painters do who think that they are showing off their draftsmanship when they draw nudes that are knotty (*legnosi*) and graceless—mere sacks of nuts." Surface anatomy overcame art on its first impact, like any discovery that novelty drives to excess. Pollaiuolo was discovering man with the eagerness of the navigators who were then exploring the shores of the expanding world. They tried to chart nothing less than the totality of man's muscles in the age when the Italian cartographers were trying to map the daily discoveries of harbors and rivers that had never seen a sail. Both cartographer and anatomist felt obliged to bring the complete crop of exploration into engravings of the anatomy of the earth and the geography of man. The two great ages of geographical discovery through the voyages of the early 1500s and through Alexander's conquests correspond to the two great ages of anatomical dis-

Fig. 30. Antonio Pollaioulo. The Battle of the Naked Men. Engraving, Florence, late 1460s.
The Metropolitan Museum of Art, New York. Joseph Pulitzer Bequest, 1917

covery. These are also the two most inventive ages of erotic art in the West, for happy discoveries inspire a hopeful curiosity about everything.

Leonardo was to continue Pollaiuolo's idea by proposing to show the body "on the same plan as Ptolemy's cosmography." Pollaiuolo's *The Battle of the Ten Naked Men* and the Ptolemy maps engraved in Rome and Bologna in the 1470s marked the first time that the thirty-year-old process of engraving was used, not for amusement or moral edification, but for the propagation of knowledge.

How did Pollaiuolo record his dissections? Not one anatomical drawing by him seems to exist today—not even in a copy—though you would think that he must have made hundreds to plot the muscles in such detail, Yet there is a chance that he may not have drawn at all for, like a proper

Fig. 31. Cornelis Cort. The Academy, after J. Stradanus. Engraving, 1578.
The Metropolitan Museum of Art, New York.
Harris Brisbane Dick Fund, 1953

sculptor, he could have modeled dissections in wax. Now if he copied every dissected muscle in a wax model and then engraved his "Ten Naked Men" from the wax figurines, every muscle would appear in the engraving whether the body's action required it or not. And if he bent his wax manikin into a pose that he then engraved from both sides, this would account for the symmetrical clash of the ten strange combatants, for the "Ten Naked Men" look a little like five men attacking a looking glass. The notion of modeling dissections in wax could have been suggested by Pliny's account of Lysistratos's wax life casts. If Pollaiuolo ever cast a muscle man in bronze, it does not seem to have been identified today, either in the original or in an old copy. If he made the first such figures, he may not have realized their usefulness to artists.

Had Pollaiuolo drawn dissections, he could have done so from bodies laid out on trestles, but if he modeled, then he would have had to walk around a body hung from a beam, as was often done later (fig. 31). In order to prevent the body from turning as he modeled, he would have had to hang it from two points such as the neck and one wrist. This would elevate an arm in a gesture of entreaty or command, or of one who is about to strike a blow, which is the basic gesture of Pollaiuolo's "Ten Naked Men" and also of every sculptured muscle man from the earliest one right through to Houdon's. Houdon's muscle man, the most famous of all, started as a study for a St. John the Baptist raising his hand to command attention as he preaches.

MANTEGNA AND THE ANTIQUE

POLLAIUOLO'S sweepstake agglomeration of the muscles might have confused more than it clarified if, at about the same time, Mantegna had not prepared a corrective from antique sculpture. In the homeland of the first archaeologists (between Milan, Verona, and Venice) the anatomy of antique marbles awoke from its thousand-year sleep in the art of Mantegna, who probably never saw a Greek sculpture but owned bits of several Roman ones. On the pavement of his St. Sebastian in Vienna (fig. 32) he twice painted a Roman marble head (probably from his own collection), which he again repeated with the colors of life as the head of the saint himself. St. Sebastian's torso, with its solid ribs and bold muscles, is simplified from Roman copies, themselves simplified from Greek originals. Such a triple remove from the living model would have chilled the end product if Mantegna had not fired it from his volcanic anger at being born too late to be a Roman. In willing himself into a vanished antiquity he had trouble shaking off his still mediaeval habits of seeing, which shows in the conflict of old and new in the saint's torso, where the Polycleitan architecture of the rib cage and the swelling S-curves linking trunk and legs are at odds with the mediaeval waist pinched by a doublet, and the ascetic arm that has no Polycleitan broad band of

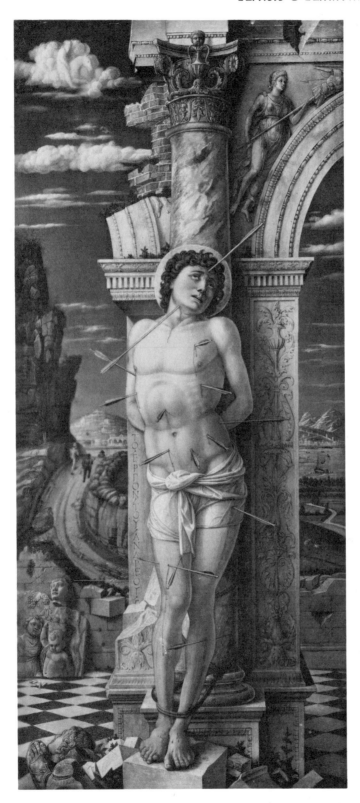

Fig. 32. Andrea Mantegna. Saint Sebastian, about 1458. Tempera on wood. Kunsthistorisches Museum, Vienna

pectoral muscle to grow it firmly to the chest. Yet the determination to be antique dominates everything right down to the signature in Greek.

Mantegna achieved much more of the compact organization of the antique in the series of great engravings which he may have begun in the 1460s while Pollaiuolo was probably engraving his *The Battle of the Ten Naked Men* a hundred miles to the south (fig. 30). While Mantegna's paintings stayed in Italy, his copperplates spread his fame abroad. (fig. 33). The popularity of his pen drawings in artists' workshops could have suggested to him that he might reach more people and make more money if, instead of selling a limited number of drawings, he published many impressions of engravings in the style of his pen work. In the 1460s when he engaged professional engravers to copy his works, he started a practice later followed by Raphael, Titian, and Rubens, all of whom built up much of their contemporary fame by advertising their work through prints, which spread a painter's style as effectively then, as magazine illustrations do today.

Mantegna freed engraving from the niggling of its inventors, the goldsmiths, by making it imitate the openness of his pen drawing and even the airiness of a sketch that dissipates before expanding to the edge of the paper. When he engraved with his own hand his graver cut the copper as freely, as vigorously as his quill exploring paper, so that other artists immediately began teaching themselves to draw by copying his prints. When Dürer was twenty-three he followed a common practice by tracing Mantegna's engravings (fig. 34). Impressions of Mantegna's prints often bear paint stains to prove their hard use near painters' easels, and his designs appear in all forms of European art for over a century. (Almost in our own time Aubrey Beardsley thumbtacked Amand-Durand facsimiles of them to his walls.) Mantegna's violence and clarity created irresistible drawing patterns for the antique grand scheme of the torso at exactly the moment when Renaissance artists needed a strong framework for organizing Pollaiuolo's wholesale revelation of the muscles.

Thus from the 1460s to the 1480s patterns and worksheets were engraved for the two great traditions of figure drawing that were to dominate Western art until about 1900—the antique tradition that Mantegna simplified for every student's use, and Pollaiuolo's brand-new experiment that anatomists and artists would have to clarify before the world at large could accept it as a way of seeing man. Pollaiuolo and Mantegna also rivaled each other at a distance in a particular project that was to exercise many artists in figure drawing. In 1460 Pollaiuolo painted Hercules heaving up the giant Antaeus, who struggles to wrench himself free so that he can renew his strength by touching his mother, the earth (fig. 35). One nude man lifting another in a grapple to the death—here was a problem in grouping and muscular action that challenged Mantegna and his circle and continued to tease artists right into the Baroque style, which the contest helped to prepare (fig. 36). The dozens of paintings, sculptures, and prints of Hercules wrestling with Antaeus seem never to borrow from antique models, but to be fresh explorations that chronicle the growth of anatomical knowledge from the earliest collaboration of artists and anatomists right through to the triumph of modern anatomy inaugurated by Vesalius and Calcar.

Fig. 33. Andrea Mantegna. Battle of the Sea Gods. Engraving (right half), about 1485–88.
The Metropolitan Museum of Art, New York. Rogers Fund, 1921

Fig. 34. Albrecht Dürer. Tritons Fighting, after Mantegna. Pen and bistre, 1494.
Graphische Sammlung Albertina, Vienna

Fig. 35. Antonio Pollaiuolo, Hercules and Antaeus, about 1460. Oil on wood.
Uffizi, Florence
Alinari/Art Resource, Inc.

Fig. 36. Hercules and Antaeus. Statuette in the manner of
Giovanni Bologna (1529–1608). Terracotta.
The Metropolitan Museum of Art, New York. Rogers Fund, 1913

ANATOMY AND PERSPECTIVE

Discovery quickened the Italian air when Masaccio and his Florentine followers began to imagine a floor plan for each painting, a real depth in which no two solid bodies can occupy the same space at the same time. To perfect this entirely new kind of picture, Italian painters had to establish a measurable space through mathematical perspective, and had to construct the body through anatomy. In the 1430s and 1440s they worked with mathematicians to find the principles of perspective, and slightly later they worked with dissectors to uncover the structure of muscle and bone. Florence thus forged the two chief tools for the realistic art of the next 450 years.

A stimulus to both discoveries came from the aspiration of painters and sculptors to better their traditional social position. Antiquity and the Middle Ages had classed them with mechanics, unfit to associate with freeborn men who might practice only liberal arts like mathematics or history because they did not gnarl his hands or hump his back or make him sweat far from the gymnasium baths. All Olympus mocked Vulcan, the forger of armor, but minded their manners before Apollo, the god of words and music. Such distinctions made sense when it was hard to bathe at home, when a Greek philosopher not only looked, but more important, smelled sharply different from a sculptor or a ditchdigger—it hardly mattered which. The first artist to become almost a gentleman was the mediaeval illuminator of books, who might also be a monk.

One of the basest of the artists was the sweaty, gritty, hammering sculptor, if one may believe Lucian's disparagement of his sculptor uncle. So it was really a notable victory when Michelangelo ennobled the sculptor at about the same time that Vesalius ennobled the surgeon, when the Renaissance gradually allowed a genius to do anything, even to imitate a slave by laboring with his hands. Michelangelo's social triumph marked the Italian artist's hard-won approach to parity with the humanist, a rise in status that Vasari consolidated by writing his *Lives of the Artists* in acceptable Italian. Italian artists marked their climbing by their names, for most of the earlier men went under nicknames or Christian names like the other servants—Pollaiuolo (Poultry Dealer), Masaccio (Big Tom), Tintoretto (Little Dyer), Rosso (Redhead)—whereas most of the later artists from Vasari to the Tiepolos achieved the dignity of family names like all writers since Petrarch.

The Florentine painters and sculptors of the early 1400s started to change the immemorial order by writing about art as brilliantly as the historians and the philosophers, by devising a perspective as intricate as any operation then known to mathematicians, and by discovering more about human muscles than the doctors. The effort succeeded beyond their hopes, for the artists' writings took on an independent life as aesthetics and the history of art; their mathematical perspective gave rise to projective geometry; their drawings made it possible to re-found human anatomy on a firmer basis of fact; and nowadays the artist himself has at last dislodged the saint from a unique shrine of personal inviolability.

Florentines discovered perspective and modern anatomy by a cross-fertilization of disciplines when artists began to collaborate with mathematicians and physicians. To achieve both discoveries the artist had to bring his omnivorous and innocent scrutiny of shapes and colors into adjustment with the scientists's logical system. Anatomy developed a little later than perspective, probably because it had to overcome qualms about dissecting. Though Vasari may be wrong in calling Pollaiuolo the first artist-dissector, he showed his usual perception of style when he called him the first modern (that is, Renaissance) master, because Pollaiuolo did indeed start modern art on its unceasing exploration of human anatomy.

Outside Florence fewer artists seem to have studied dissection, although a masterly Venetian (Gentile Bellini?) was obviously drawing from his own observation when he illustrated the Venetian edition of Mondino's *Anatomy* published (with other works) in 1491 (fig. 8). These woodcuts show no muscular dissection that could help an artist, but their firm and lucid drawing set a standard for future scientific illustration.

When the crossing of disciplines was producing mathematical perspective and modern anatomical drawing, these new disciplines crossed in turn to apply mathematical perspective to the impossible irregularities of human anatomy. Piero della Francesca worked out a madly complex procedure for projecting the human head in foreshortening as though it were a Doric capital, and Uccello's dead warriors are whole bodies much more simply foreshortened. A copy of Piero's manuscript may have come to Dürer who published a woodcut of a very similar head in 1528. Dürer's print probably passed the clumsy notion on to Jean Cousin, who projected the entire body by plan and elevation in his drawing book of 1560 (fig. 37). But these bleak curiosities produced at least one great work of art in 1506 when Mantegna painted perhaps his last picture, the violently foreshortened Dead Christ (fig. 38). A baroque etching adapted Mantegna's scheme (fig. 39) and brought it to Rembrandt for his second anatomy lesson of 1656 (fig. 40) where he dodged the worst difficulties by hollowing out the thorax and shrouding the thighs.

Mantegna opened a whole new world in 1469–70 when he foreshortened clothed and naked figures to make them seem to be looking down a hole painted in a low ceiling in the palace at Mantua. Here he applied perspective to anatomy to create the first of those apparent enlargements of space that were to become the glory of baroque rooms. Later painters, acquiring anatomical virtuosity from Michelangelo and Vesalius, elaborated on Mantegna's hint by opening the whole ceiling to the sky and populating clouds with men and women and weightless babies who swing their legs over the void as if to prove themselves divine by flaunting an indifference to dizziness.

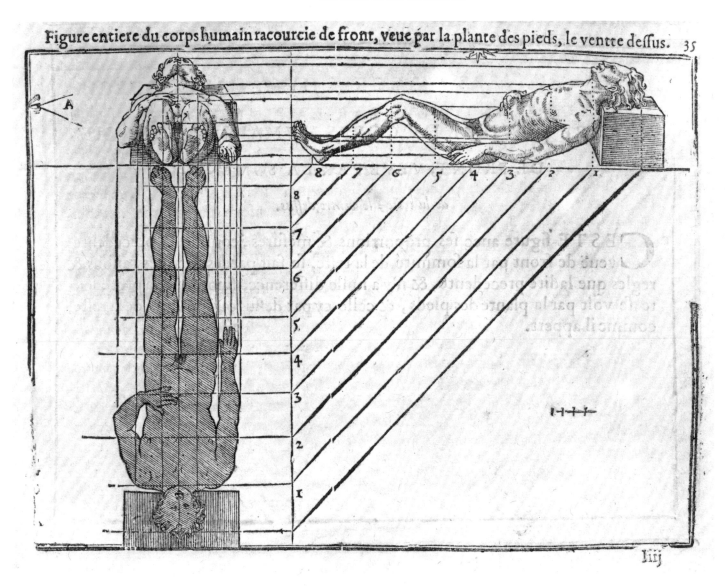

Fig. 37. Woodcut illustration in Jean Cousin, *Livre de pourtraicture*,
Paris (Guillaume le Bé), 1560. From 1656 edition.
The Metropolitan Museum of Art, New York

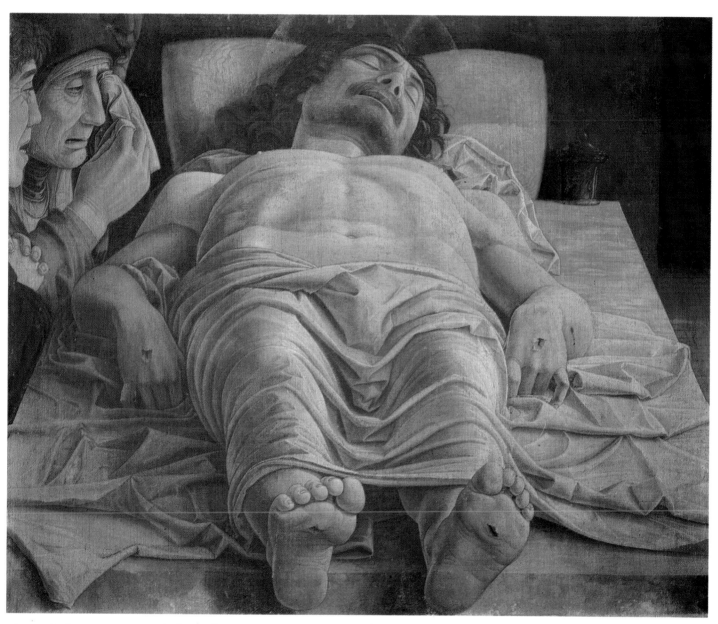

Fig. 38. Andrea Mantegna. Dead Christ, after 1501. Tempera on canvas.
Pinacoteca di Brera, Milan
SCALA/Art Resource, Inc.

Fig. 39. Orazio Borgiani. Dead Christ and the Three Marys, 1615. Etching.
The Metropolitan Museum of Art, New York.
Harris Brisbane Dick Fund, 1926

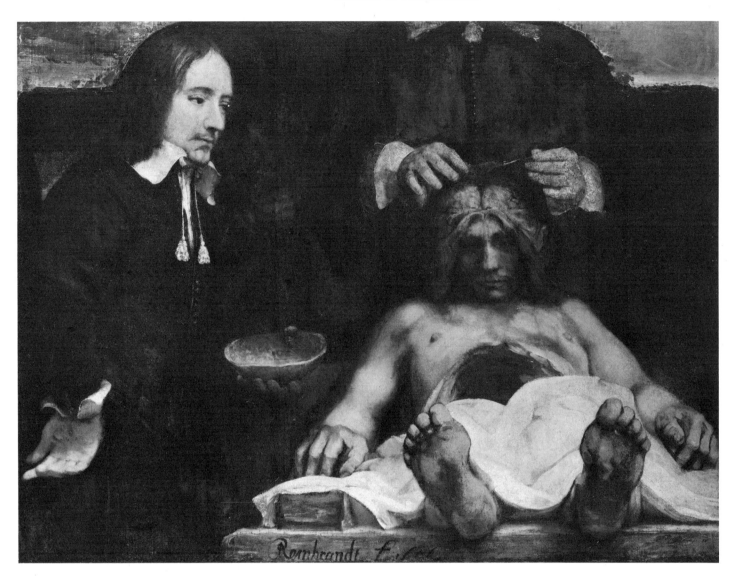

Fig. 40. Rembrandt van Rijn. Anatomy Lesson of Dr. Joan Deyman, 1656. Oil on canvas, fragment.
Rijksmuseum, Amsterdam

LEONARDO DA VINCI

LACKING any Pollaiuolo drawings of dissections, we find that the oldest surviving group of great anatomical drawings is by Leonardo. He must have begun by dissecting like Pollaiuolo to investigate the bones and surface muscles which he had to know in order to become an up-to-date painter of nudes in action. Later, when anatomy began to fascinate him as an end in itself, he explored beyond the needs of art, for what painter ever has to show the liver or the lungs? Leonardo planned a book to show the development of the body from infancy to old age, and another to show the shape and situation of each part by drawing it from the front, side, and back. These would have been the first of the modern scientific books in which the pictures tell more than the text. Such methodical expositions for science went so far beyond Leonardo's scanty formal schooling that he never completed any of his plans, but investigated hither and yon as whim and chance suggested. Luckily, no scholastic drilling put serious blinders on his direct observation, but this happy lack also left him without a framework of logic for organizing anatomy into an intellectual discipline. So in spite of his originality, his insight, and his draftsmanship, he could not alone have founded anatomy as a modern science. It is fascinating to speculate on what he might have achieved if Marco della Torre, the anatomist who collaborated with him for five or six years, had not died young in 1512.

Not that Leonardo scorned the learning of the schools. Quite the contrary, like many men who never attended a university, he overrated scholastic authority and followed Mondino's text so humbly that he sometimes drew formations that exist nowhere except in Galen's or Mondino's writings. Also, accepting the Galenic theory that man and some animals have practically interchangeable organs, he would draw a human fetus in a cow's uterus, or a bull's larynx in a man's throat. (The larynx is perhaps a special case, for even Vesalius usually had to demonstrate it from farm animals because most of his human specimens had been damaged by hanging or beheading.)

Yet Leonardo's shortcomings cannot dim the splendor of his achievement. His anatomical drawings are more than the first accurate ones, for their delicate vitality has never yet been rivaled. This lonely observer noting things for himself drew quickly, accurately and cleanly, with no flourish to impress another eye, until he mastered the beauty of an exquisite utility. His practice as a designer of mechanical wings and of catapults, which are mechanical arms, enabled him to discover the body as a living machine and to draw the engineering of bone and muscle with a livelier action than any artist has ever achieved. He was quite aware of his then unique approach, for he said that an anatomist must "understand the methods of geometrical demonstration and the method of the calculation of forces and of the strength of the muscles."

Leonardo was the first anatomist who thought more about a muscle action than about its

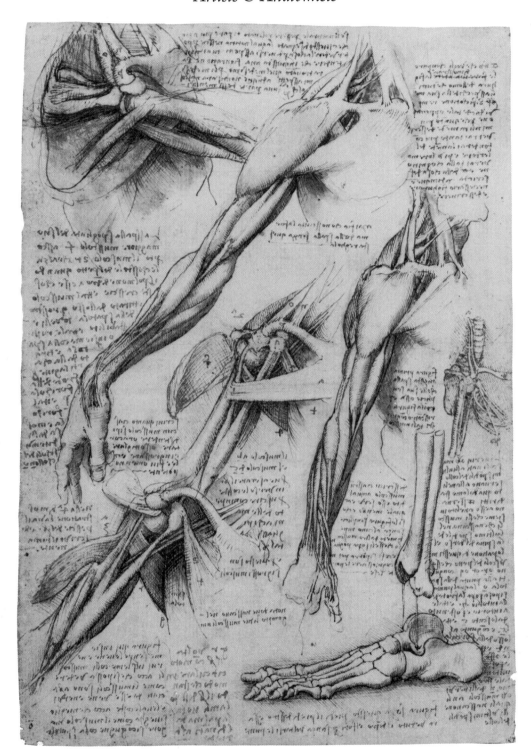

Fig. 41. Leonardo da Vinci. Myology of the shoulder region, about 1510. Pen and brown ink.
Royal Library, Windsor Castle

shape and situation, and who therefore drew muscles as ropes pulling levers of bone. So when he analyzed the action of the arm (fig. 41), he did not draw it as a dead dissection, but as though the fluoroscope of his imagination showed him the living bones crossing and uncrossing as the hand reaches out for food and then twists back to put it into the mouth. Dissection did not detain him among corpses, but led him into the life of the body more deeply than any artist before or since. At twenty-one, he was already probing into the laws underlying appearances when he drew a view of the valley near his birthplace, which shows him analyzing mountain slopes for the geologic erosion of their musculature.

It does not matter that Leonardo lacked the academic system to do what Vesalius and Calcar were later to do as a team, for he had a rarer gift. He was the first man who, having found the plan in a limp confusion of tissues, and having unraveled the track of a wet thread of nerve, then could draw his exploration so unmistakably that his drawings can forever guide any dissector in comprehending the structure in a tangle that opens under his knife. He originated something much more inventive than his machines, which initiate no mechanical principle, something even more basic than a systematic anatomy, for he discovered how to describe nature through a classic compromise between a copy of appearances and an abstract diagram of connections understood by the intellect. Without the insight of such analytical picture-making much of modern science could not exist, for the camera cannot think. The discipline of difficult seeing enriched his art with an intellectual fascination that art has since lost by losing contact with science. For Leonardo, art and science, far from clashing, joined in one exploration of the visible world; science needed the artist to observe and draw, and art needed science to formulate principles to which art should conform. The natural sciences have adopted Leonardo's methods of drawing so totally that we cannot imagine science functioning without them, and we cannot realize Leonardo's originality because it now looks inevitable, like the sun at noon. While almost all of Leonardo's scientific drawings lay unpublished until 1898, they were studied by so many Renaissance men that they must have helped to set the new standard of intellectual drawing without which John of Calcar could never have given visual form to Vesalius's system of anatomy.

MICHELANGELO

For some seventy-five years anatomy inspired Florentine artists as much as the dream of Greece and Rome. After Leonardo every enterprising Florentine artist had to observe at least a smattering of dissection. Some, like Rosso (fig. 42) and Michelangelo, followed him by planning books on artistic anatomy that came to nothing, like Leonardo's own projects. Michelangelo said that he lacked the style and dignity to write a book on anatomy, a diffidence that shows how humbly he approached the study of man's body, even though it sounds forced from a writer whom some foreigners value as Italy's second poet. By "style and dignity" he must have meant that he lacked academic system as much as Leonardo, for he did not choose a writer to help him with his book but a physician, Matteo Realdo Colombo.

This physician, Colombo, collaborated toward the book by supplying Michelangelo with at least one body, that of a shapely young Moor, and by writing to Duke Cosimo I de' Medici on April 17, 1548 for leave to absent himself from his teaching post at the University of Pisa (except during the midwinter anatomy demonstration) so that he could stay in Rome to work on his book "with the world's foremost painter." He reported that "much has been accomplished, and this summer the skeleton will be attended to." This sounds as though the project were still not much more than a hope, and as though Colombo had received little co-operation from Michelangelo, for the anatomist also writes that he wants to work with "painters" in the plural.

Was Colombo using art as a pretext to persuade the Medici—patrons of anatomy as well as of art—to let him quit stagnant Pisa for the pomp of Rome? Or did he wish to launch his book by attaching it to a great artist's name? Whatever were his schemes, in the end he published *De Re Anatomica* in 1559 alone, and with no scientific illustrations at all, without even an apology for their absence.

None of Michelangelo's talk about the human body may survive in the anatomist's text, for Colombo was too busy refuting Galen and Vesalius to remember his unforgettable friend. He names dozens of prelates and princes who crowded demonstrations, but never mentions any artist whatsoever, although the woodcut frontispiece to his book shows a lad sketching the cadaver that Colombo is anatomizing in the midst of robed and bearded worthies. Colombo's double vanity as pedant and as parvenu must have obstructed collaboration at least as much as Michelangelo's hermetic bitterness. Yet a mere word of the artist's graphic talk might echo in Colombo's comparison of the spine to a ship's keel from which the human ribs branch out like the ribs of a ship. This homely simile refreshes a book that tries to expound a descriptive science without one picture.

Bernini said that anatomy obsessed Michelangelo as though he were a surgeon. Michelangelo

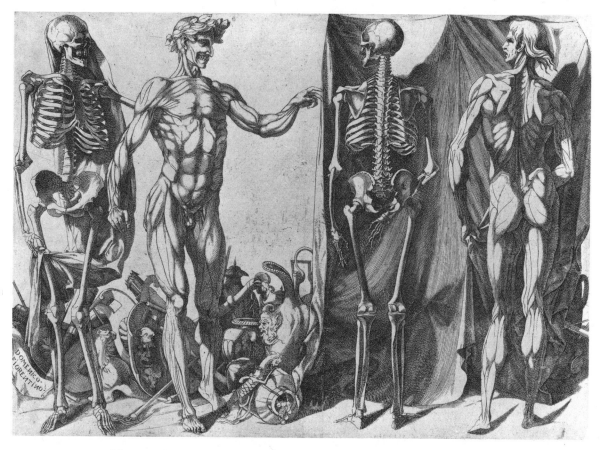

Fig. 42. Domenico del Barbiere. Two Flayed Men and Their Skeletons, after Rosso. Etching, before 1530.
The Metropolitan Museum of Art, New York.
The Elisha Whittelsey Collection, The Elisha Whittelsey Fund, 1949

started dissecting when he was about seventeen and continued off and on for years until he looked into every living body as into a package of structure and, conversely, imagined every dissection in lively action, which makes it often impossible to tell whether he is drawing from a model or a dissection (fig. 43). He certainly must have made many out-and-out anatomical drawings, but so few survive that he must have destroyed them systematically in the gloomy bonfires that he lit whenever his drawings piled up. Indeed he may have thought that dissection uncovered a nakedness beyond nudity, fit for study but not for art, because some such modesty seems to have led him in the *Last Judgment*—that least modest of church pictures—to represent St. Bartholomew still dressed in his skin while clutching a second skin—or a borrowed skin—like a draped raincoat (fig. 44). The limp features that sag from his hand reappear in the frontispieces of several baroque anatomy books.

In 1746 Pierre-Jean Mariette said in his observations on Condivi's *Life of Michelangelo* that he owned "several studies" for the Risen Christ in the Minerva in which Michelangelo had "drawn

Fig. 43. Michelangelo Buonarroti. Studies of arms and hands for
the *Dying Slave*; dissection of arms. Red chalk and pen.
Teyler Museum, Haarlem

Fig. 44. Michelangelo Buonarroti. Saint Bartholomew. Detail of the *Last Judgment*,
1536–41. Sistine Chapel, Rome
SCALA/Art Resource, Inc.

Fig. 45. Michelangelo Buonarroti. Studies for the *Libyan Sibyl*. Red chalk.
The Metropolitan Museum of Art, New York.
Purchase, Joseph Pulitzer Bequest, 1924

a skeleton and, after adjusting the main tones to the action of the figure, had clothed them in muscles, then covering these muscles with flesh." So specific a description by so keen a connoisseur must mean that these drawings were indeed by Michelangelo, but where are they now? The only recorded drawing for the Risen Christ does not look as though it could have belonged to this series, and Mariette's sale catalogue tantalizingly lumps all his forty Michelangelo drawings in one unitemized lot.

Being less inquisitive and more practical than Leonardo, Michelangelo probably cut no deeper than he had to in order to attain his supreme command of the massing of muscle on bone. Man's anatomy underlay his whole art so completely that he enlarged on a Vitruvian maxim by writing: "The members of architecture depend on the members of man. One must excel in drawing figures and especially dissections in order to understand architecture." Because he thought of buildings as living beings, his roughest architectural jutting breathes and moves almost as much as Leonardo's drawings of bones.

Man (but not woman) was never so much the measure of all things, not even among the Greeks. Michelangelo studied a man's evident structure even when he was preparing to paint the more enveloped body of a woman (fig. 45). He rebelled against antiquity in almost everything except the Greek ideal of love and the literature that justified it. Most classical Greeks, Romans and Renaissance Italians thought of the beautiful nude as a man, but the beautiful nude became a woman when Italian art was imported into France in the 1540s and entered the climate of troubadour poetry. Indeed, the French have exploited the cult of woman in all the arts. Corneille, Racine, and Molière are the first great playwrights who ever wrote for actresses and, more recently, Maillol modeled girls in the attitudes of Greek statues of youths. The general trend is as clear as it is in the sexual preferences of an individual. It would seem as though a woman's pearly subtlety of skin sets the problem for any style that tends toward color, whereas a man's muscular and complex structure sets the problem for styles of sharp definition. Certainly woman ruled Venetian painting from Giovanni Bellini to the Tiepolos, and man preoccupied Mantegna, Donatello, Signorelli, and Michelangelo.

Michelangelo's anatomical drawings betray a heaviness of labor entirely unlike Leonardo's deft lightning, a massiveness that weights the impact of his effort (fig. 46). He drives his figures at you, plunges you so deep into their blind visceral battles that you feel that their bodies are your body. Is this perhaps the secret of his famous *terribilità*? Is it the terror of being drawn into the dark struggling of the muscles against the bone? Michelangelo discovered nothing less than a new way for the body to move. Action ceases to be a single lunge of impulse, as when you throw a ball or run or jump. A figure by Michelangelo contradicts itself through actions that clash against each other and cancel out into inaction. The legs run counter to the torso, which wrestles against the arms, while the head twists distractedly away from the whole struggle. The deeper the tussle invades the body, the more desperate it grows, until muscle fights muscle to a deadlock. Those

Fig. 46. Michelangelo Buonarroti. Studies for the *Crucified Haman*, 1511. Red chalk.
Teyler Museum, Haarlem

bandages that he strapped around the limbs or chest are hoops to keep the scuffle from exploding. Such a checkmate of forces that kills action could not be further removed from Greek equipoise, nor could it have been discovered by the earlier Greeks who saw the body as an animal organized by action and existing only for the purposes of action. Michelangelo could hardly have constructed his interlocking of unbalance unless Alberti had already separated the body into layers, and Leonardo had diagramed muscle as a motor pulling against the lever of bone. The intensity of Michelangelo's conflict forces his figures into the foreground of our attention and projects them closer to our eyes than any figures in all art. In his marbles he pushes the bulk of his creatures right up into our faces with the overcoat of roughness which acts like the blur that fuzzes a thing held too close to be seen clearly.

When Michelangelo's *Last Judgment* was unveiled in October 1541—two years before the publication of Vesalius's *Fabrica*—that cataract of suffering flesh astounded Europe. For the first time in history those plunging, soaring somersaults demonstrated the nude in all sorts of acrobatics that no live model can hold. We know little of Michelangelo's labors of preparation because he hid them, but he could have studied such tumblings by the methods of a sculptor, by modeling a wax model and dangling it from a beam as Tintoretto, who learned so much from Michelangelo, did in order to fly his painted angels. Any later painter could have modeled such study manikins quite simply from Vesalius's handy woodcuts. Michelangelo's ultimate demonstration of anatomical omniscience, and Vesalius's immediately following publication of the first convenient and informative series of prints of bones and muscles together started painters catapulting figures into the zenith and launched the baroque conquest of the air.

During Michelangelo's lifetime engravings brought his Sistine frescoes to the world at large, but reproduced less of his sculptures. The few statues that left Italy landed in out-of-the-way places like Bruges and Fontainebleau, so that most people north of the Alps must have known him at second hand as a painter. The French and Spanish sculptors who studied in Italy naturally picked up his attitudes, but it was not until Rubens that an artist penetrated beyond his manner into the source of his vitality.

RAPHAEL

I N R O M E from about 1510 until the Sack in 1527, Marcantonio Raimondi and his helpers engraved and published many drawings by Raphael and his school. These engravings must have sold briskly, for some reproduced Raphael's fresco designs before he had revised them in the process of painting. Marcantonio's engravings established the typical Italian print as a reproduction of a great painter's mythological scene composed usually of nudes almost always in action. Even though Marcantonio sometimes added clothes and distracting backgrounds (figs. 47, 48), his inexpensive, easily packed tourist souvenirs advertised the greatness of Italian figure drawing as they scattered across Europe. They did more than carry Raphael's fame outside Italy and make him the most celebrated Italian painter—they swept across Europe like a fire of the mind, consuming the Gothic style and replacing it with the High Renaissance in the sudden revolt of one generation. Northern artists and the general public welcomed Italian prints as warmly as those

Fig. 47. Marcantonio Raimondi. The Massacre of the Innocents, after Raphael. Engraving, about 1513–15. The Metropolitan Museum of Art, New York. Gift of Felix M. Warburg and His Family, 1941

quick-rich magpies, Henry VIII and Francis I, welcomed Italian artists dislodged by the Sack of Rome. European art never again broke so abruptly with tradition until shortly after 1900 when the abstract styles exploded.

Raphael was perfectly equipped to teach the Florentine way of drawing the figure, for Vasari says that he trained himself out of his master Perugino's old-fashioned manner by studying anatomy through dissection. By adopting a modern style during his maturity he may have smoothed some of the personality out of his art (as Dürer certainly did out of his) but by exploring for himself through adult reason instead of being taught by childish rote, he achieved a style so understandable that it can teach anyone. The pressure of production forced him to construct figures swiftly with guidelines and rules of thumb, like the heads that he quartered like lemons by scoring them down through the nose and across through the eyes. He certainly cannot have been the first to prepare for a painting by drawing skeletons, but his skeletal study for *The Entombment* (1507) (fig. 49) seems to be among the oldest now surviving. His schemes are so practical that they serve as well today as they did in the 1520s.

Fig. 48. Raphael. The Massacre of the Innocents, about 1509. Pen and brown ink, with red chalk. British Museum, London

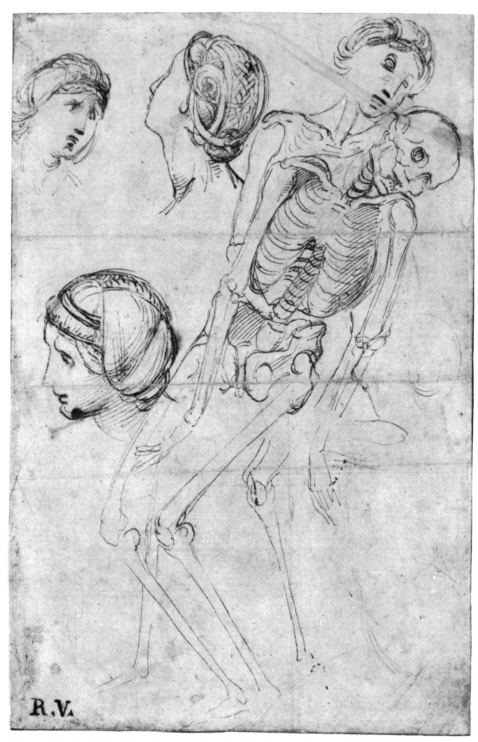

Fig. 49. Raphael. The Virgin Supported by the Holy Women: Anatomical
Study for the Borghese *Entombment*, 1507. Pen and brown ink over black chalk.
British Museum, London

Raphael perfected the delicate and thoughtful Italian art of painting figures from recollection and from sketches of the model. Every painter's handiest model was his apprentice, whose smooth young slenderness rules Italian art before Michelangelo with the insolence of adolescence, so that most quattrocento nudes must be portraits of the next generation's great painters as lads. Vasari mentions the common practice of drawing from the nude in summer, when it was comfortable to pose, in order to paint from the sketches in the cold of winter, and Leonardo says that on winter evenings young students should select the best of the summer's studies of limbs and bodies so as to apply them in practice and memorize them. Such drawings are not show pieces but aids to memory that make the artist observe penetratingly summer notes. The remembrance of the model clarified the winter's painting by forgetting details, thus enabling Italian artists to achieve a reasonable reconsideration of the body such as the Greeks achieved by haunting the gymnasium. Raphael brought this lucid Italian drawing to its full beauty. As his pen went exploring it described form under a control as easily and inevitably as water flowing around a rock, in a subtlety of slipstream that is an imitator's despair.

No wonder that the prints after Raphael, Giulio Romano, and Rosso overran the West with the advance news of the High Renaissance. Italian figure drawing so satisfied the French that they have followed it ever since in their official art, where throughout the centuries Raphael's equipoise blends in varying proportion with Giulio Romano's erudite sensuality and Rosso's elegant acrobatics to produce the figures of Jean Goujon, Boucher, Ingres, and Matisse.

DÜRER

CONTINUING northward, streams of exportation from Italy naturally attracted northern artists southward to the Italian sources in Venice and Rome. Dürer, the first northern artist determined to Italianize himself, was the only artist who ever changed in mid-career from the Northern Gothic to the Italian Renaissance style and produced memorable works in both. In order to re-educate himself he had to master that basic Italian achievement, the anatomy of man, through a struggle in the course of which he studied Italian figure drawing from Pollaiuolo and Mantegna to Raphael. He inquired so extensively into the practice of Italian artists that he must have heard about the Florentine artist-dissectors, and he could have watched the midwinter anatomies in Tübingen or Venice, but some invincible revulsion must have checked him and forced him to try every roundabout substitute. Yet if he could simply have learned from dissection to think of the body as a mechanism of bone and muscle, he would have thrown out most

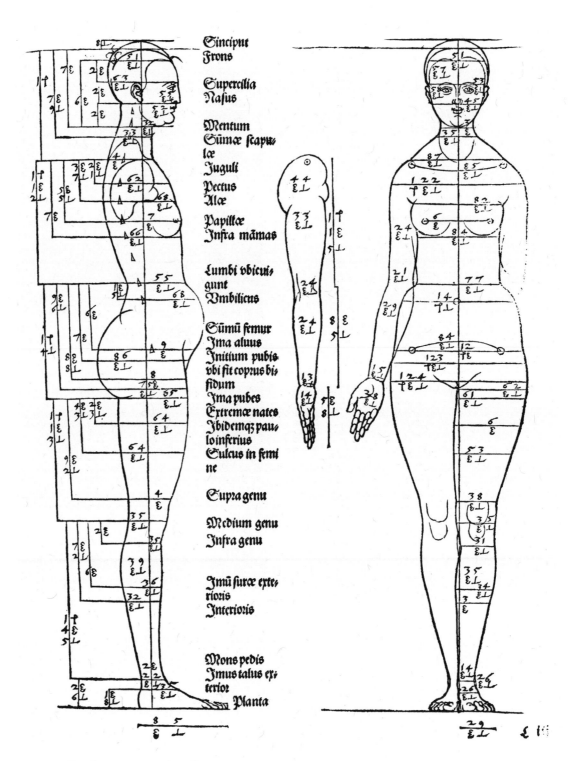

Fig. 50. Albrecht Dürer. Woodcut illustration in *De Symmetria Partium . . . Humanorum Corporum*, Nuremberg (Widow of the artist), 1528. From 1532 edition.
The Metropolitan Museum of Art, New York. Gift of Felix M. Warburg, 1918

of the inventions that his baffled ingenuity kept restlessly inventing with a waste of effort that is confusing even to list.

Five years before he died he wrote the touching story of his search. As a young man, perhaps on his first trip to Venice, he had met that graceful second-rate painter Jacopo de' Barbari. "He showed me the figures of a man and a woman, which he had drawn according to a canon of proportions, so that at that time I would rather have seen what he meant than be shown a new kingdom. . . . I was still young and had not heard of such things before. However, I was very fond of art, so I set myself to discover how such a canon might be wrought out, for this Jacopo, as I clearly saw, would not explain his principles to me. So I set to work on my own and read Vitruvius, who writes somewhat about the human figure. Thus I took my start from these two men, and thence from day to day I have followed up my search according to my own notions."

De' Barbari could not have told Dürer much about the Florentine dissectors, for the sleaziness of his own figure drawing shows that he had shirked the long hard labor needed to master anatomical structure. The secret that he refused to tell was probably some version of Vitruvius's intricate table of proportions for the well built man considered in terms of the well-designed façade. "From the chin to the roots of the hair is a tenth of the body's height. From the chin to the crown of the head is an eighth of the whole height," etc. Vitruvius's rather confused account of a common studio practice might go back, through Polycleitus and other Greeks, to the network of squares that the Egyptians used for fixing the proportions of man, beast, and bird in order to standardize their picture writing into types as legible as our printed letters. The Egyptian grid served well for figures laid out in flat profile, but became useless as soon as Greek painters began to foreshorten the figure. Vitruvius tabulated the most elaborate rules of proportion surviving from Antiquity, and imposed them on the Renaissance through his canonical authority. Leonardo showed his independence by making a system of his own by measuring adjacent parts of the body against each other ("from the angle of the eye socket to the ear is as far as the ear's length, or one third of the face"). But, probably after coming to the north of Italy, he drew the most famous of all the pictures of Vitruvian proportions. These antique proportions were much discussed in Venice, then the center of antiquarian and architectural studies, during the very years when Dürer and de' Barbari were there.

De' Barbari's Vitruvian notions started Dürer off on the sort of elaborate arithmetic that Italians used more often for architecture than for figure drawing. Yet what was a foreigner to think? Now that Italians were creating the first splendid, active nudes since classical antiquity, would not a newcomer like Dürer naturally assume that they were able to do so by exploiting some antique formula of proportions like those that they were brilliantly adapting for their buildings?

About 1500 someone, possibly de' Barbari, must have shown Dürer sketches of two antique statues recently unearthed in Rome, for he began drawing human proportions based on the

Apollo Belvedere (fig. 72) and the weary *Hercules* of the Borghese. The slenderness of the *Apollo* and the stockiness of the *Hercules* must have shown Dürer that antiquity had not adhered to any single canon of proportion. What then was de' Barbari's secret?

Dürer obeyed a healthy instinct by returning to nature and measuring hundreds of men, women, and children—tall and short, fat and thin—and then tabulating the averages like a Renaissance Dr. Kinsey (fig. 50). The science of statistics did not start, as is sometimes stated, with the tabulation of the bills of mortality of the London plague of 1665. It started about 1500 with Dürer. His systematic calculations sobered his art with a synthetic impersonality, for he was older than Raphael when he changed his manner, and he revised it so much more radically that the wrench disrupted even so eager a versatility as his. Of course nothing could entirely remove the sting of excitement from his electric spirit, but it is fascinating to speculate on how he might have developed had he met Leonardo da Vinci instead of Jacopo de' Barbari. Supposing that Leonardo could have broken Dürer's "scientific" obsession with ruler and compass, then the jagged Gothic energy of his youth could have gathered a still higher voltage from the fresh experiment of artistic dissection, from probing into the individual right down to the universal bone.

Dürer saw Leonardo's work without understanding what he was driving at, for in all of Dürer's varied writings he never mentions the structure or function of any bone or muscle. In his Dresden sketchbook he copied an existing Leonardo drawing of striding legs and leg bones, and he probably copied lost Leonardos in a horse study, a head of an ugly man in an Italian cap and collar, and in a pair of contrasting and overlapping profiles (beak over pug) showing the typical Leonardesque clash of antipathies. There are also equally Leonardesque diagrams of muscles like rubber bands stretched over the bones of the leg, arm, and hand (fig. 51). These tidy, flat, inaccurate outlines could not have been drawn in front of actual dissections, for nobody could cluster some fifteen wrist bones while looking at the eight in an actual skeleton, or could arrive at such an abstract scheme of muscles without studying them long enough to summarize them more accurately.

Yet Dürer would have found it hard to avoid seeing dissections sometime or other. The government of Venice had decreed annual public anatomies in 1368. In 1491, about the time of Dürer's first trip there, the city printed Mondino's *Anatomy* with woodcuts that the splendid, unidentified illustrator—certainly an acquaintance of Dürer's—must have drawn from sketches made at an actual dissection (fig. 21). If leading Venetian artists were watching anatomies, Dürer's omnivorous curiosity must have pushed him in among them. The point is not that Dürer never saw a dissection, but that he failed to understand how dissection could serve a realistic art, and so concentrated on outline and proportion (the designer's invention) instead of structure and mechanism (the observer's study). While this did not matter in the early Gothic dreams and visions, it began to matter basically as soon as he attempted Renaissance naturalism, aiming at Italian ambitions without understanding the preparation that enabled Italians to achieve their ambitions,

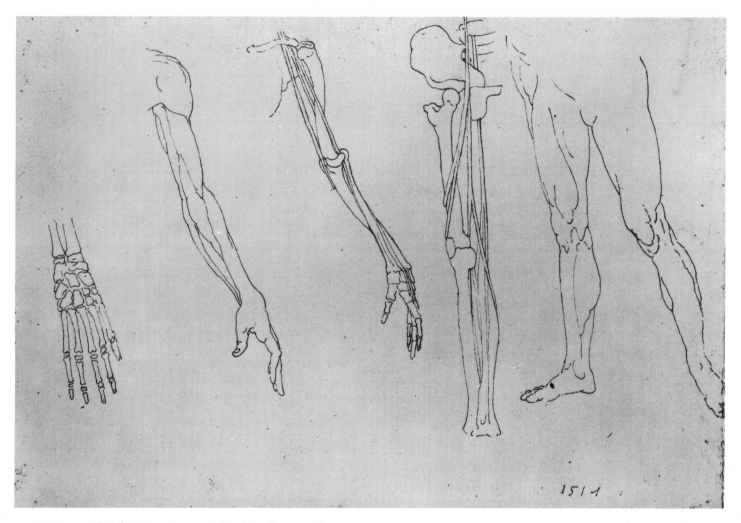

Fig. 51. Albrecht Dürer. Anatomical studies of arms and legs.
Pen and ink drawings in the *Dresden Sketchbook*, fol. 130b

just like Hokusai in his nudes. His failure to understand shows in every line that he drew in later life when compared with Leonardo's drawings (fig. 41). Leonardo's lines always describe, always hug the roundness of a shape, always follow wherever structure leads. Dürer's lines create a manly arabesque that is almost as independent of nature as calligraphy or music. He is, in all art, the supreme, ultimate, hypnotizing doodler. Francis Bacon said "trifler."

Dürer showed how little his eye explored below surfaces when he copied Mantegna's engraving of the *Sea Gods* (figs. 33, 34). Mantegna constructed the woman's back like a strong sculptor. Dürer traced her outlines accurately, inside of which he filled in a confusion of free-hand details that indicate no structure or function under the skin. Mantegna's defensive horse's skull becomes a skein of loops. Dürer's famous drawing aids, the frame of glass and the string network, help a painter to trace a monocular map with neat boundaries, and to outline a figure, but not to

Fig. 52. Albrecht Dürer. Figure study in pen and ink from the
Dresden Sketchbook, fol. 137

Fig. 53. Woodcut illustration in Erhard Schön, *Underweissung der proportzion*, Nuremberg (Zell), 1538.
The Metropolitan Museum of Art, New York. Harris Brisbane Dick Fund, 1946

Fig. 54. Nicolas Poussin. The Holy Family, about 1648. Pen and bistre wash.
Pierpont Morgan Library, New York

model its roundness or to understand its inner structure. (Leonardo also knew about drawing aids, but corrected them from other studies.) Dürer, adjusting edges with calipers, achieved details that explode by the excitement of their silhouette, so that his pictures scatter into something less than the sum of their parts.

Dürer established his outlines by using geometric schemes of triangles, squares, arcs of circles, or grids. Sometimes he divided heads with horizontal lines as the Gothic architect Villard de Honnecourt had done in about 1250, probably following a very ancient shop practice. All these schemes answer the question: "How can I rough out a figure?" Most of Villard's mediaeval schemes serve the mediaeval fascination with analogy and allegory by asking: "How can I fit a face inside a leaf or around a star?" In the more pragmatic Renaissance, Dürer was always trying to be practical, even when he divided the body into units of 1/600 of the total height.

At least one of Dürer's drawing schemes has lasted until today. This is his assemblage of elegantly disjointed manikins out of stacks of boxes pivoting around a pliant axis (fig. 52). Nearly a century earlier, Paolo Uccello in Florence had painted warriors in armor as assemblages of simple geometrical solids, and who knows if some of his now lost drawings may not have come into Dürer's hands? Dürer's box construction was published for every artist's use in Erhard Schön's dramatic drawing book in 1538 (fig. 53) after which it reappears in designs by Cambiaso and

Fig. 55. Etching by Francesco Bartolozzi in Giovanni Battista Piazzetta, *Studii di Pittura*,
Venice (Albrizzi), 1760. The Metropolitan Museum of Art, New York.
The Elisha Whittelsey Collection, The Elisha Whittelsey Fund, 1949

Poussin (fig. 54). It is attractive to think that Dürer might have helped to shape cubist painting
from 1905 to 1910, but that movement came out of African carvings and other theories. Yet who
can be sure that the latent memory of Dürer's cubism might not have predisposed Europeans to
discover beauty in African and pre-Columbian sculpture? This would do a kind of justice to
Dürer, who was one of the first Europeans to admire Aztec art.

Dürer, like Leonardo, considered the proportions of the baby. The ancient Greeks had
regarded children as imperfect projects for adults, unfit to speak in tragic dramas, but the Renaissance accepted the child's chubbiness as one stage in the wholeness of man. The child's emotions
had to wait until Freud to be studied as seriously as Leonardo and Dürer did its body. Yet in spite
of the Renaissance interest in the baby's anatomy, cupids did not flutter in quantity until the
Counter Reformation hatched them in swarms for its campaign of blandishment. Then, after
about 1575, altars, ceilings, and drawing books pullulate with pudgy hands, shy smiles and tubby
little rumps (fig. 55).

The only practical effect of Dürer's rules and schemes was to slacken the German Renaissance
and to tame its breathless revelations into the skillful and charming correctness of the Little Masters.

DRAWING BOOKS AND ACADEMIES

Shortly after Dürer's death in 1528 his labors of some thirty years were finally printed in Nuremberg by his widow in *Four Books of Human Proportion* (fig. 50). This intricate rumination on figure drawing was translated into several languages and eventually appeared in Italian in Venice to bring de' Barbari's original impulse home full circle. Michelangelo and other Tuscans thought the work useless, but several Germans extracted practical bits and popularized them in little books on drawing. These modest manuals appeared in countless editions, of which only a few copies have survived, thumbed and tattered as painters searched them for the kind of anatomical information that they were later to get much better from Vesalius's great anatomy. The first and most popular of these little manuals was Hans Sebald Beham's (1528), which merely plagiarized Dürer's published and unpublished drawing schemes. Erhard Schön's box manikins have already been mentioned (fig. 53).

The only early German drawing book quite outside Dürer's influence sets forth no methodical program of study, but offers scraps of designs to be patched in wherever needed, like Villard de Honnecourt's random notebook of three centuries earlier (fig. 25), or like many of today's do-it-yourself manuals. This curious scrapbook of bits and pieces was published in Strassburg in 1537 by Heinrich Vogtherr, who stated his purpose thus: "Out of brotherly love for artists burdened by wife and children and for those who have not travelled, I have published a little gathering of exotic and difficult details full of fantasy and cogitation to the end that dull heads be spared, and artists of high understanding be cheered and inspired." Vogtherr's thirty-one pages of outlandish headdresses, hands (fig. 56), feet, and fantastic weapons and armor appear in minor sixteenth-century works of art wherever poor artists stuck them in when their skill broke down. Such spare parts for quick and easy attachment made the usefulness of many Baroque drawing books where post-Vesalian realists heaped up giblets on copperplates as heavily laden as cold platters (fig. 57).

Some such job lots of classified features probably also served in schools, for in 1593 Federigo Zuccaro offered at the Academy of St. Luke in Rome to teach "the ABC of drawing—eyes, noses, mouths, heads, hands, feet, arms, torsos, backs, etc." This first Roman academy must be represented in the engraving, *The Painters' School*, that Pierfrancesco Alberti made in Rome about 1600 (fig. 58). In this earliest print of art students in a classroom, a scholar at the left submits his drawing of eyes to a bearded teacher who might be Zuccaro himself. The shelf holds a row of plaster casts of antique statues, of the head of one of Michelangelo's *Slaves* and of the hand and foot of his *David*. Here, in one of the first art classrooms, the *David* has already begun to impose itself serially as the standard copybook Hand, Foot, Nose, Eye (and Eyebrow).

But the study of separate parts did not produce an understanding of the whole, as Vasari

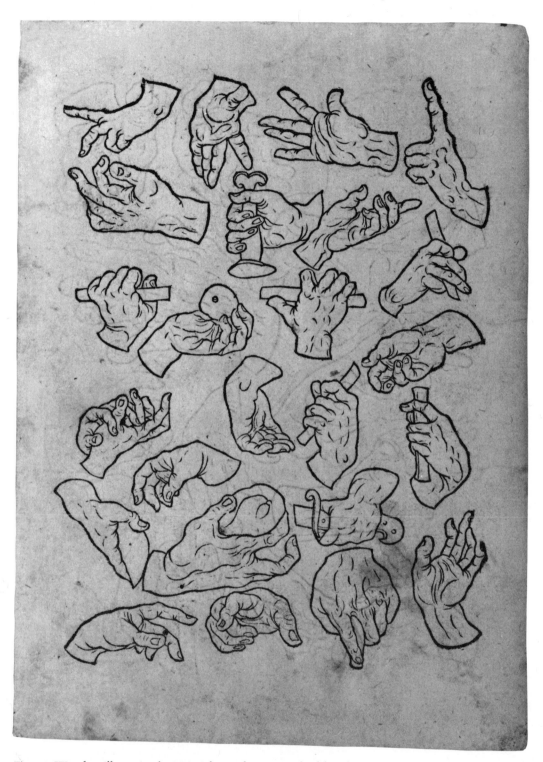

Fig. 56. Woodcut illustration by Heinrich Vogtherr in *Ein frembds und
wunderbars Kunstbüchlin . . .* , Strassburg, 1538.
The Metropolitan Museum of Art, New York. Rogers Fund, 1919

Fig. 57. Engraved illustration by Giacomo Franco in Giacomo Franco and Jacopo Palma II,
Regole per Imparar A Disegnar, Venice (Sadeler), 1636.
The Metropolitan Museum of Art, New York.
The Elisha Whittelsey Collection, The Elisha Whittelsey Fund, 1949

Fig. 58. Pierfrancesco Alberti. A Painter's Academy in Rome. Engraving, about 1600.
The Metropolitan Museum of Art, New York.
The Elisha Whittelsey Collection, The Elisha Whittelsey Fund, 1949

intelligently stated when he said that Battista Franco (whose drawing book we have seen—fig. 57), "wasted time beyond all reason over the minutiae of muscles . . . Painters delude themselves if they concentrate on perfecting a torso, an arm, or a leg with well studied muscles, because a part of the work is not the whole, and perfection is attained only by fitting well-made parts in due proportion to the whole."

About three years after Zuccaro offered to teach "eyes, noses, mouths, etc." at the Roman Academy of St. Luke, the academy opened the first formal art school with a modern curriculum of classes. Alberti's engraving (fig. 58) shows what is practically a school initiation as the established scholar, his first maulstick in his hand, opens the door to a new boy who timidly presents his letter of introduction and gets his hat knocked off to teach him manners. Beside and above the entering freshman hang plaster casts of what seem to be a flayed head and leg, while to the right students are dissecting a cadaver. The print is probably the first picture of a skeleton mounted on a stand according to Vesalius's method, and the classroom needs only a blackboard and Houdon's muscle man to make it contemporary.

By 1607 the Academy of St. Luke was offering a course in *anatomia*, though it omits the subject in its first curriculum of about 1596. However, its students probably dissected from the start, for in 1578, before the founding of the Academy, an engraving after Stradanus shows Roman prentices—*tyrones picturae*—already studying the skeleton and the flayed body (fig. 31). The suspended body hangs from a single rope so that the artist-dissector can turn it easily to point out what the boys should draw. The boys are studying muscles and bones from human beings, but the nude from casts of the Medici *Venus* and the *Tiber* on the Capitoline. Until quite modern times art students did not study the living nude until they had learned enough anatomy to interpret the structure hidden under the discrete indications on the body's surface. It would be fascinating to know how Greek artists were trained at various periods.

BERENGARIO DA CARPI

R ENAISSANCE artists failed to establish modern anatomy in spite of knowing human bones and muscles better than the doctors. A Renaissance doctor succeeded no better when he corrected Galen, but with amateurish illustrations. This attempt at reform was made in 1521–23 when Giacomo Berengario da Carpi published three anatomical books which he may have illustrated himself. Cellini, who knew this rich, astute, artistic physician in Rome, says that he collected paintings and "understood drawing" (*aveva molte intelligenze del disegno*). This does not clearly state that Berengario could draw, and he does not appear in Vasari's lives of professional artists of the day, but even if he could not draw, Berengario must at least have cared about the illustrations in his books. He improved the woodcuts in each successive book, and he had several of his illustrations cut twice on two different woodblocks which both reproduce the same figure with varying success.

Berengario began by publishing a commentary on Mondino's *Anatomy* in Bologna, which he immediately amplified into an independent treatise that ran through two editions in two years. Though the three books were forgotten twenty years later in the uproar over Vesalius's *Fabrica*, Berengario's modest and peculiar woodcuts deserve attention because they pointed out the direction that anatomical illustration was to follow for several centuries. They were the most numerous anatomical illustrations so far published, and must have done much to popularize the books.

Fig. 59. Woodcut illustration in Berengario da Carpi,
Isagogae breves, 1522.
John Martin Rare Book Room,
Health Sciences Library, University of Iowa

Part of Berengario's illustrations are small woodcuts of practical anatomical details, and part
are more decorative full-page figures (fig. 59). These big woodcuts look like the work of an
amateur unable to invent figures but clever enough to adapt creations by professional artists. Thus
one of the big figures is Michelangelo's *David* carrying a rope instead of a sling, and in another a
backward-leaning nude from the Sistine ceiling is bungled into a woman. Elsewhere there is a
copy of Giorgio Ghisi's engraving of Neptune. The pregnant woman (fig. 59), derives from the
Venetian Mondino of 1491 (fig. 8), seated on a birth stool with her head drooping like a dying
Niobid or a dead Adonis on a Roman sarcophagus. A type of antique Roman terracotta lamp
supplied the skeleton who holds up two skulls like an athlete raising dumbells (fig. 60). But
Berengario invented something new in the series of jaunty young men who pull away the flaps
of their skin so as to help us to inspect their stomach muscles, with a courteous gesture that
reappears in several Baroque anatomy books (fig. 61). Berengario's muscle men are fairly accurate

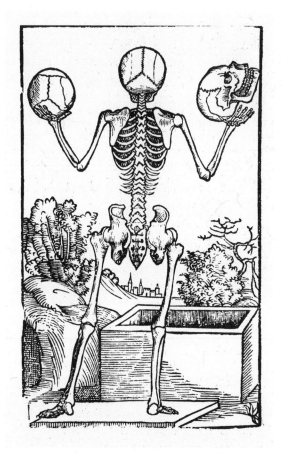

Figs. 60 and 61. Woodcut illustrations in Berengario da Carpi, *Commentaria . . . super anatomia Mudini*, Bologna (Benedictis), 1521. New York Academy of Medicine Library

when they are based on contemporary works of art, but his skeletons go wild because he had the harder task of copying nature.

In the smaller woodcuts Berengario followed Leonardo's methods so closely that he may have copied Leonardo drawings for the brain, the heart, the bones of the hand and foot, and above all for the illustration of the arm with its veins, seen from the front, side, and back as in Leonardo's scheme (fig. 62). Leonardo had drawn many parts of the body in isolation, but Berengario was the first to put such into print. He facilitated study by printing the name of each part right beside it, an aid that Vesalius would have done well to have adopted.

But Berengario lacked Leonardo's grasp of the scientific usefulness of pictures. His text refers only casually to his illustrations, and the two sometimes disagree, as when he writes that there are twenty-four vertebrae, and illustrates twenty-six. Above all, he did not realize that pictures would have conveyed his many accurate and original observations more effectively than words. Yet

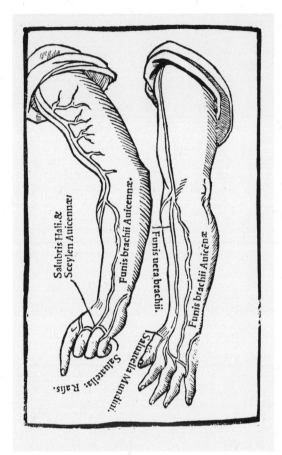 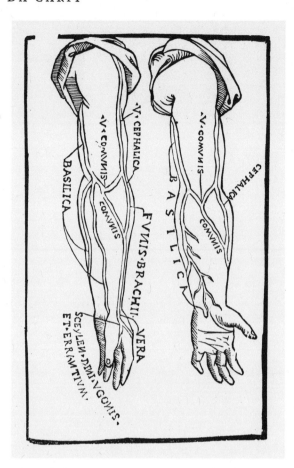

Fig. 62. Woodcut illustrations in Berengario da Carpi, *Commentaria . . . super anatomia Mudini*, Bologna (Benedictis), 1521. New York Academy of Medicine Library

this doctor-connoisseur understood art well enough to publish the first anatomy that is intended at least partly for artists, for in a marginal note he explains that his illustrations can be useful to surgeons "and will also help painters to draw limbs." Elsewhere he observes that "skillful painters study and understand the stomach muscles."

What was the purpose of Berengario's illustrations, which the French anatomist Sylvius called a *farrago sumptuosa*? The smaller studies of separate parts give helpful information, but the full-page figures with muscles badly copied from good works of art are useless decorations thrown in "to beguile eyes that cannot read," as Brunschwig said in his book on distillation in 1500. These stupid comments on scientific illustration point up Leonardo's originality. In the end, Berengario may matter because he discovered that dissected figures can declaim like tragedians, and because he was the first professional anatomist to bring anatomical illustration in touch with art, even if he did so merely by adapting works that his age admired.

93

CHARLES ESTIENNE

BERENGARIO's book suggested several features that appeared in a strange anatomy book that was being prepared in Paris by 1530 or earlier, though it was not printed until 1545. This was Charles Estienne's *De Dissectione*, whose startling woodcuts fall into three categories. The book opens with some stiff skeletons that must have been drawn, like all pre-Vesalian skeletons, from bones laid flat on the floor. Then follow dissections of the brain and thorax displayed by men who collapse in contortions like cadavers half raised on ropes for the inspection of a class. C. E. Kellett has suggested that these figures might derive from the lost anatomical manuscript that Rosso brought to France in 1530 in the vain hope of getting it published. The broken figures certainly look as frantic as most of Rosso's, and one crawler (fig. 63) could have been cut from a sketch for the fallen warrior in Rosso's painting, *Moses Defending Jethro's Daughters*. However, the book shows no muscle men paired with skeletons, both posed in identical attitudes, like those in what might be the only surviving illustration to Rosso's lost book, engraved by Domenico del Barbiere (fig. 42). But the strangest series is the third, of the female organs demonstrated by ladies sitting on chairs, as in Berengario's cut of the pregnant woman—or rather, not sitting, but sprawling in elegant, inexplicable levitation (fig. 64). Dr. Kellett has pointed out that these ladies lack visible means of support because eight of them are made up from Caraglio's engravings of the *Loves of the Gods* by merely copying each goddess without her supporting or encircling god. Rosso again seems to lurk in the background, because he designed one of the engravings adapted in Estienne's book, the other seven coming from Perino del Vaga. Berengario had supplied the basic idea of seating a female anatomical figure on a chair, but his dramatic presentation lost its appropriateness when his useful Italian birth stool was turned into fancy French court furniture.

No one has ever explained why Estienne's dissected organs appear on small squares of wood plugged into the full-page woodblocks. Presumably the anatomy had to be corrected when Vesalius brought out his book two years before Estienne's—and yet Estienne nowhere copies Vesalius. No impressions are known before the insertion of the plugs.

Berengario and Estienne show that an anatomist could not advance science much by adapting some handsome pictures or by using art as decoration or background. A pure artist helped science more when he drew dissections, even though he did not know how to organize his studies into a systematic and general demonstration. This last step required a long partnership between an artist and an anatomist, both equally strong in their specialties.

CORP. HVMANI LIB. II. 253

Exempta sunt omnia, quæ
ossibus capitis contineban-
tur, nempe tota cerebri sub-
stantia, & quicquid neruo-
rum, venarū & arteriarum
ad caput pertinebat. Tātum
hac figura vides ea forami-
na, eósque sinus, qui post ex-
emptum & ablatum cerebrū
in interioribus ossibus cōspi-
ciuntur.

R.j.

Fig. 63. Woodcut illustration by Etienne de la Rivière in Charles Estienne, *De Dissectione partium corporis*, Paris (Simon de Colines), 1545.
The Metropolitan Museum of Art, New York. Harris Brisbane Dick Fund, 1942

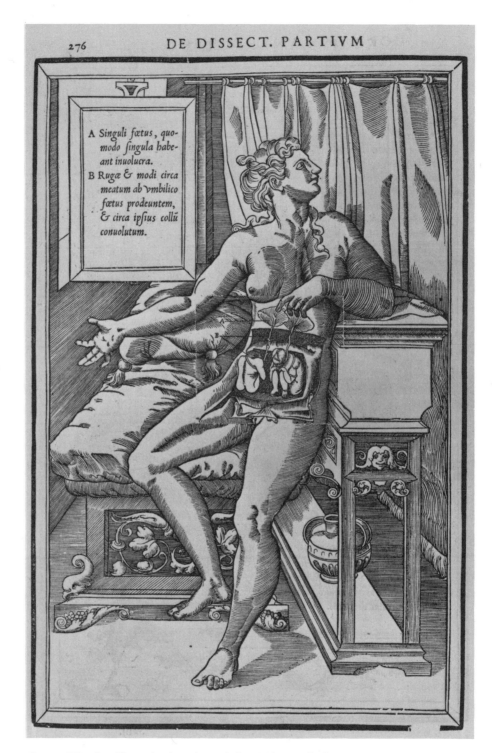

Fig. 64. Woodcut illustration by Etienne de la Riviére in Charles Estienne,
De Dissectione partium corporis, Paris (Simon de Colines), 1545.
The Metropolitan Museum of Art, New York. Harris Brisbane Dick Fund, 1942

VESALIUS AND JOHN OF CALCAR

QUITE SOON after Berengario an event occurred that was to eclipse his brief popularity, was to distract attention from Dürer's surface measurements and solid geometry, and was to instruct artists at a deeper level than the cheap little German manuals. This new creation was achieved like Dürer's by systematic northerners coming into contact with Italian art.

To describe the body systematically in word and picture an anatomist had to establish a general scheme for an artist to illustrate. Neither specialist could do it alone, for the anatomist could not draw well enough or observe with the artist's unprejudiced directness, and the artist had no logical system around which to organize his perceptions. Teamwork had then hardly begun among scientists, although today it has become the normal procedure, winning its most spectacular triumphs in nuclear physics and medicine. Today teamwork has practically disappeared from painting, but in the early 1500s a successful artist ran something like our decorators' shops by directing a varied group of craftsmen who could supply an altarpiece, a brooch, a triumphal arch, a painted chest, a portrait, or an embroidery. When finally an anatomist was able to join the kind of a team that was normal for an artist, the new team—perhaps the first of its kind in the world— created modern anatomy at one step, by making word and picture advance like a pair of legs striding toward discovery.

Berengario, among others, had written corrections to Galen, but had made little stir because he did not illustrate his discoveries adequately. But when Vesalius corrected Galen by describing many illustrations, the combination of text and pictures touched off an intellectual explosion.

Someone someday will investigate why people have made pictures. The first pictures must have been the kind of signs that develop into writing, marks that say things like "Joe went this way." The cave men drew themselves killing bison to coerce nature, wishful pictures like the medals of St. Christopher that motorists hang up to protect their automobiles from accident. Probably much later, pictures were made for decoration. We continue to make pictures for signs, magic, and decoration, but in the Renaissance the Italians, who had been drawing and carving longer than the rest of Europe, finally intellectualized the sign pictures to make them communicate scientific information and discovery. Italians were able at that moment to turn pictures into a language of the intellect because their towns, especially Florence, had so many secondary schools that their craftsmen like Ghiberti and Piero della Francesca wrote Italian with some ease. These literate craftsmen inspired less contempt than their Greek and Roman forebears from contemporary writers on art like Alberti and Daniello Barbaro, who also mastered the practice of the arts that they expounded. But in spite of all their visual subtlety, it would have been hard for two Italians to undergo together the routine drudgery needed to create modern anatomy, because

Italian artists invent so incessantly that future projects tend to distract them from carrying through a present labor. How hard it has often been to persuade an Italian painter or sculptor to deliver a commissioned work!

Vasari praises Italian artists for invention as often as Van Mander praises northerners for high finish, for northern Europeans have excelled in the arts of spit-and-polish, such as Netherlandish engraving or French ormolu, and in demonstrations pursued to their interminable consequences like Dürer's measurements of the human figure, late Gothic tracery, or Bach's *Art of the Fugue*. The definitive demonstration of anatomy by word and picture became possible when northern scholastic logic and naturalistic exactitude made themselves visible through Italian intellectual draftsmanship.

The words and pictures needed for modern anatomy were combined by an anatomist and an artist who were both born in Flanders about fifteen years apart and came at about the same time to Venice or nearby Padua. We know a great deal about the anatomist Andreas Vesalius because he justified himself and vilified his colleagues in voluminous print after he became an intellectual storm center for Europe. But we know little about the artist-illustrator, John Stephen of Calcar, because he left no letters nor so much as a signature on a drawing or a painting. Posterity had naturally tended to credit all to the anatomist and to forget the artist. Actually neither could have succeeded without the other.

When the teen-age Vesalius was studying anatomy, he ran into obstacles that he luridly described at the end of the *Chyna Root Letter*: "In Paris I handled bones for many hours in the Cemetery of the Innocents and went with a companion through murdering packs of dogs to see corpses on the gallows at Montfaucon. In Louvain I prepared a skeleton from bones that I stole at midnight from the gibbet." His passion for anatomy inevitably led him to the rising scientific center in the University of Padua, where dissections were as much a routine as lectures. A Renaissance man was equally at home in any university because the universality of Latin made for a cosmopolitanism—lost today—which was the last living survival of the ancient Roman unity of Europe. The University of Padua welcomed Vesalius by making him full professor of anatomy on December 6, 1537. He was only twenty-two.

Anatomists before Vesalius had noticed that Galen did not always describe exactly what their knife uncovered, but they usually explained the discrepancies by assuming that copyists had distorted Galen's text or that man's body had changed since ancient times. Dissection convinced Vesalius that Galen had been wrong in assuming that man and certain animals had interchangeable organs. As he put it, "Galen's monkeys tricked him." Anatomy had to begin all over again from the human body. When he was twenty-four, a year and a half after arriving in Italy, he published his first results in an unevenly illustrated pamphlet, the *Tabulae Anatomicae Sex* (1538), showing the blood vessels and the skeleton in six woodcuts. His full labors appeared in his epoch-making folio *De Humani Corporis Fabrica* in 1543 when he was twenty-nine. A man of one book, he lived on to be fifty without adding to his achievement.

His main illustrator, John Stephen of Calcar—also a man of one book—was about fifteen years older than Vesalius. Since Calcar apparently did not leave his native Netherlands until his early thirties he must have had a thorough grounding in the exact detail of Flemish art. But once settled in Venice he absorbed Titian's style so completely that his paintings, if any survive, must be lost among the mass of Titianesque work. After drawing anatomical illustrations for Vesalius, he went to Naples, and soon died.

Calcar was certainly Vesalius's chief illustrator, but it is not so certain just where his work begins and ends. He published Vesalius's first illustrations, the *Tabulae Sex* of 1538, under his own name and drew its three stiff, inaccurate skeletons. Of the other three illustrations, Vesalius himself wrote: "I drew the diagrams of veins and arteries (*vasorum ductus*) with my own hand (*meo Marte*)." Five years later the many woodcuts in the *Fabrica* appeared unsigned, but Vesalius wrote in a letter that Calcar was helping him. Two years after the *Fabrica*, Calcar told Vasari that he had drawn the illustrations. Vasari reported in his *Lives* that "the eleven full-page dissections (*notomia*) were made (*fatte*) by Andreas Vesalius and drawn (*disegnate*) by John Calcar the Fleming." Vasari, who often mistakes dates and figures, must mean the fourteen muscle men of the *Fabrica*. It is odd that he should not have mentioned the skeletons which certainly look to be by the same hand. They may have been drawn first, before someone had the happy thought, which was used in the muscle men, of making backgrounds that can be joined together in two continuous landscape strips (figs. 65, 66).

When Vesalius once mentioned his "illustrators" in the plural he might have meant Calcar and the unnamed woodcutter who helped to pack the woodblocks for shipping to the printer. But there is the fascinating possibility that his "illustrators" might have included no less a man than Titian, whose supreme hand could well have created the relaxed, grand figures of Adam and Eve (figs. 67, 68), which move with a more Olympian swing than any other Vesalian illustrations and are the only ones that are drawn with Titian's own sensitive splendor. The *Fabrica* cuts were pirated at Bologna in about 1670 as *Titian's Anatomy*, and this late, otherwise unimportant attribution may perhaps be supported by a word from the minor wit Annibale Caro, who to be sure never lived anywhere near Vesalius but at least corresponded with Titian's friends, Aretino and Paolo Manuzio. In a squib called *La Statua della Foia* written at about the time of the *Fabrica*, Caro compares fragments of statues to "Titian's dissections" (*la notomia del Vecellio*). Dr. Tietze-Conrat suggested that Titian might have outlined the muscle men in attitudes suggested by the antique statues that he admired, which Calcar would then have filled in with anatomical detail under Vesalius's direction. If this is right, then Vesalius would have had a hand in all the pictures of dissections, but not in the undissected *Adam* and *Eve*, which he did not publish in his scientific

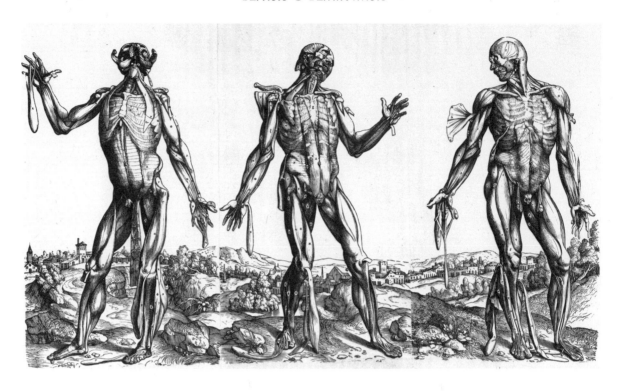

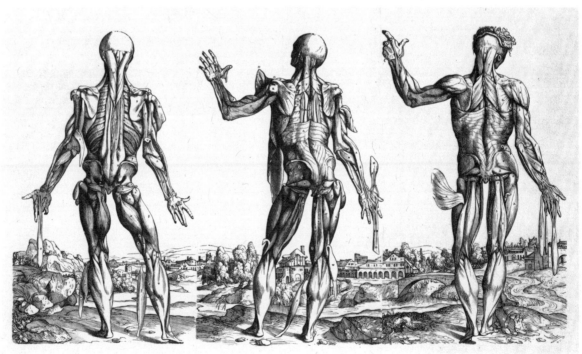

Figs. 65 and 66. Woodcuts by John Stephen of Calcar for Andreas Vesalius, *De Humani corporis fabrica*, Basel (Oporinus), 1543. (Restrikes, 1934).
The Metropolitan Museum of Art, New York. Gift of The New York Academy of Medicine, 1947

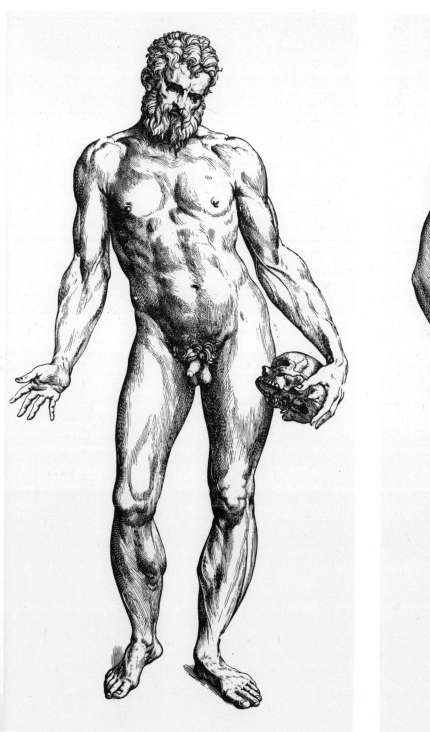

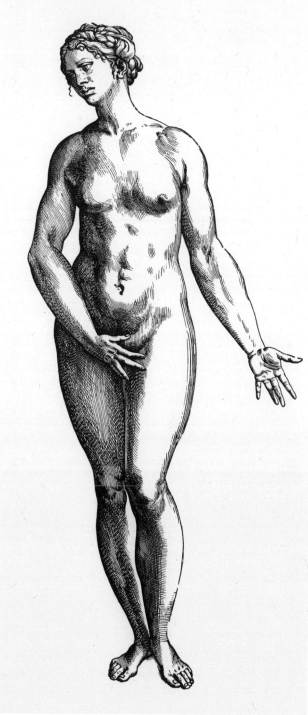

Figs. 67 and 68. Adam and Eve. Woodcuts, probably after Titian, in Andreas Vesalius,
Epitome, Basel (Oporinus), 1543. (Restrikes, 1934).
The Metropolitan Museum of Art, New York. Gift of The New York Academy of Medicine, 1947

books but only in the layman's summary of the *Fabrica*, called the *Epitome*, as though these cuts were marginal decorations fit for the general public but not for the professional anatomist. All evidence in the way of letters and preparatory drawings must have perished a year after the publication of the *Fabrica* when Vesalius burned his papers in a rage at his critics.

It would be strange if Titian had *not* made himself felt in major Venetian illustrations of the 1530s and 1540s, for he pervades the best Venetian woodcuts of that age as clearly as Botticelli pervades Florentine woodcuts of the 1490s, though both influences are hard to document. Titian's example and direct participation rescued the Venetian woodcut from the mechanical production of the 1510s and 1520s and sent it to the heights that made the Venetian book the model for all Europe.

Though the triumphant young professor of anatomy realized that he could not deliver his labors to the world without an artist's help, he must have found it hard to appeal to one. Not that he lacked contact with artists—quite the contrary, for he wrote in his *Chyna Root Letter*: "As for the sculptors and painters who crowd into my demonstrations, I will not let their criticism (*morositas*) exasperate me into feeling myself their inferior." Artists had for so long known the bones and muscles more accurately than the anatomists that they had assumed a cockiness which understandably galled the first Renaissance anatomist who discovered more than the artists. Yet Vesalius could probably compose his animosity when actually working with an artist, for his diagrams of the blood vessels show that he drew neatly enough to understand a draftsman's problems. An artist, on his side, could meet an anatomist half way in Renaissance Italy where the intellectual climate often involved artists in science. Vesalius would have found it easier to collaborate with a fellow countryman, almost a neighbor, like Calcar to whom he could speak in Flemish, because few artists spoke Latin like the university men. Vasari, for instance, thought it an exception worth mentioning when Rosso learned Latin to prepare for going to the court of France.

Yet despite their common nationality, the two Flemings must have had their rough moments, for Vesalius wrote that his book would progress "if cadavers are forthcoming and the Flemish painter John Stephen does not balk." They may have quarreled by the time the woodblocks were shipped to Basel in August 1542, for Vesalius does not mention Calcar among those who packed them. Indeed, it is hard to imagine why Vesalius should have sent his blocks and manuscript away from Venice, then the world's most enterprising and modern printing center, unless he had broken with vital collaborators there. It is odd to think that a clash of personalities may have deprived Venice of publishing what would have been the masterpiece of its long series of scientific books. Yet the *Fabrica*, in spite of being printed in Basel, remains a great Venetian book, for the woodcuts were made in Venice or Padua, and Venetian book and type design then dominated Swiss printing.

It was lucky for Vesalius that he found an artist who had mastered the great Venetian tradition of drawing. Venetian painters had learned from Mantegna to draw figures roundly and grandly

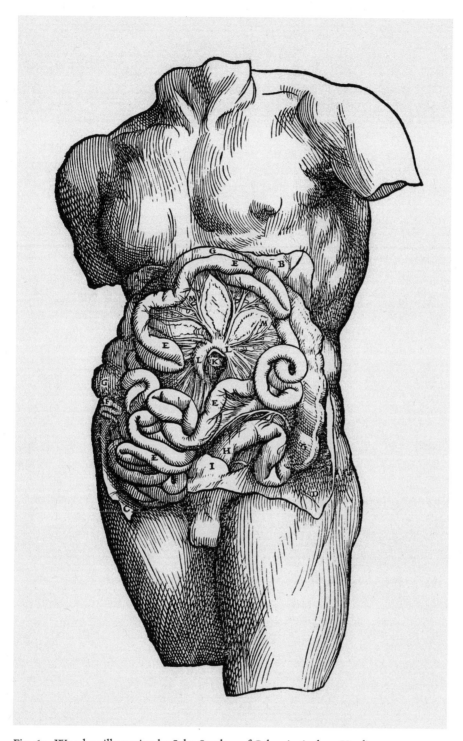

Fig. 69. Woodcut illustration by John Stephen of Calcar in Andreas Vesalius,
De Humani corporis fabrica, Basel (Oporinus), 1555.
The Metropolitan Museum of Art, New York.
Gift of Dr. Alfred E. Cohn, in honor of William M. Ivins, Jr., 1953

in a style which Titian then developed into a triumph of sensuousness and intelligence that exactly suited Vesalius's purpose. Thus the name of his illustrator matters less than the fact that he saw with the eye of Mantegna and Titian, and that their hands guided his hand. After gathering strength from the antique, north Italian drawing was now serving a partnership of artist and anatomist such as Florentines had tried in vain to yoke together.

Clear, intelligent drawing can help a scientist to perceive something in nature and can be essential for communicating his discovery to others even in our age of photography. When Vesalius wanted to illustrate any given dissection, he must have discussed with his illustrator just what aspects to clarify to make the picture play its part in a general survey of the body. The artist must then have experimented to find exactly which angle and lighting would bring out what the anatomist wanted. And then—the real test of awareness—the artist had to consider the infinite ways of drawing even a box or a ball in order to choose just those lines that describe the stressed aspects with unmistakable distinctiveness. The resulting picture must look "real" and yet be almost as selective as a diagram. In this difficult task of understanding and then of drawing so as to convey the understanding to others, Vesalius's illustrator attained almost the clarity of Leonardo da Vinci. Leonardo's drawings are more swift and exquisite; they move with a subtler flexibility, but they are hardly plainer than the bold flowing lines of Calcar's woodcuts.

So many of Leonardo's innovations reappear in the *Fabrica* that Vesalius or Calcar must have been among the many who studied Leonardo's notebooks before 1591, when most of them disappeared into Spain and then England. Leonardo's "tree of the veins" must have suggested the diagrams of the blood vessels that Vesalius drew after quickly dissecting them and drying them on a tabletop. Leonardo's sawn bones, his manner of isolating separate organs in blank space and drawing them from the front, side, and back, his presentation of opened abdomens in torsos like truncated antique statues (fig. 69), his ability to give breath and movement to muscle men and skeletons, above all his basic, revolutionary idea of expounding anatomy through a series of pictures with a commentary of text—all these discoveries that Leonardo made from the 1470s to about 1510 now reappeared in the *Fabrica* of 1543.

The *Fabrica* also owed something to Berengario da Carpi's woodcuts of some twenty years earlier, for Calcar made something both useful and handsome out of Berengario's handsome but useless full-page cuts of muscle men and skeletons, and out of his useful but unhandsome small cuts of isolated parts of the body. Most important, the *Fabrica* gave classic form to Berengario's presentation of muscle men and skeletons by bringing them into complete harmony with the drama of Renaissance art.

If Vesalius needed Calcar to deliver his message to the world, Calcar needed Vesalius even more to stimulate him with that challenge of difficulty that stung him to surpass himself. His woodcuts, which are some of the most generative pictures in all Western art, may well have been made by an artist who was at all other times mediocre. Certainly where he seems to be on his own in the portrait of Vesalius in the *Fabrica*, he botched it with a top-heavy head and disordered composition.

Vesalius did not arrange the order of his demonstration in Mondino's practical sequence of decay, but harked back to Galen's Greek logic by considering the body in strata of bone, muscle, veins, etc., and then went beyond Galen by expounding his thesis with the strict organization of St. Thomas Aquinas developing his theological system. If it had been unillustrated, or as unintelligently illustrated as Estienne's *Anatomy*, Vesalius's scholarly text would have remained in the classroom along with Estienne's. Vesalius's illustrations, however, were often copied without his text because they dramatized science so unforgettably. Since their appearance, European art has never been quite the same.

Calcar achieved his success by a method exactly opposed to Estienne's illustrator, who practically lost the viscera in the vast surrounding garnish of Renaissance furniture and knickknacks (fig. 64). Vesalius's illustrator (or illustrators) permitted no clutter to distract attention from the human actors looming up against a blank sky (figs. 65, 66). This dramatization is more old-fashioned than Leonardo's earlier but more modern demonstration of the body as an engine of gears and levers functioning in emptiness. But Vesalius and Calcar, living in the wars of religion, were perforce involved in the atmosphere of theology and so could not see the body as an impersonal mechanism. They felt, more than thought, that man's body was a house not made with hands—God's fabric created to dominate the world. So their skeletons and dissected figures are not dismembered and abject like death's mediaeval victims, nor do they demonstrate piston thrust and pulley tension like Leonardo's diagrams. They are actors strutting in the pride of life.

The very skeletons of the *Fabrica* deploy their bones with passionate grace as one bends its back and wrings its hands like a weeping Magdalen, while another leans on a monument to contemplate a skull with a scrutiny that may well have said to Shakespeare "Alas, poor Yorick" (fig. 70). In the Renaissance even the diagrams of the veins and nerves suggested a drama that John Donne expresses in *The Funeral:*

> "For if the sinewie thread my braine lets fall
> Through every part
> Can tye these partes, and make mee one of all . . ."

Unlike the skeletons, the muscle men stand upon a landscape that joins woodcut to woodcut in two friezes, one of eight men who face you and another of six who turn their backs (figs. 65, 66). This enabled an anatomist to paste the fourteen muscle men together in two strips to decorate his classroom or study. The idea of lining up a parade of anatomies could have occurred to Vesalius during his Parisian student days in the Cemetery of the Innocents, where the surrounding cloister was painted with the most famous of all the mediaeval Dances of Death. These long-vanished wall paintings probably left their record in Marchant's woodcut *Dance of Death* of 1490 (fig. 71) which spreads out like the Vesalian frieze.

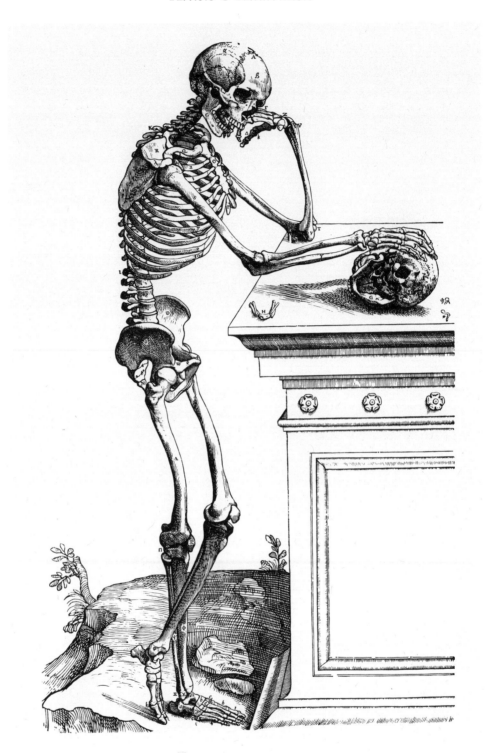

Fig. 70. Woodcut illustration by John Stephen of Calcar in Andreas Vesalius, *De Humani corporis fabrica*, Basel (Oporinus), 1543. (Restrike, 1934).
The Metropolitan Museum of Art, New York. Gift of The New York Academy of Medicine, 1947

Fig. 71. Woodcut illustration in *La danse macabre*, Paris (Marchant), 1490.
The Metropolitan Museum of Art, New York, Harris Brisbane Dick Fund, 1929

Vesalius's muscle men keep up their tattered ballet just as long as they keep their outer muscles, and only after these are cut away do they allow themselves to stagger and collapse. They triumph over the mediaeval Dance of Death with a Renaissance Dance of Life. It would be hard to find any other pictures that so unmistakably proclaim the determination to keep going despite everything, the will to live—come what may!—which distinguishes Western man from the world of Buddhism. The Alexandrian vivisectionists themselves could not have been more fascinated with living action. Nor could they have come closer to the drama of Hellenistic sculpture than Calcar's muscle men, who are not flat and reduced like wet cats or real dissections, but flex their stripped biceps like Olympic victors and strike virile antique attitudes as superbly as the *Apollo Belvedere* which then and for centuries afterward embodied the perfect figure that every artist had to learn (fig. 72). The Vesalian muscle men are not literal copies of antique statues, any more than they are copies of actual dissections, but their most frequent attitude is the antique stance of prayer of the Greek bronze *Idolino*, which then was the prize of the Medici collections. It is as though Calcar (or Titian?) had posed the muscle men to act as celebrants in an invocation to life.

Antique sculpture, however, appears undisguised in some of the smaller woodcuts of the *Fabrica*, as it does in three Leonardo sketches at Windsor. Both the woodcuts and the drawings show abdominal dissections encased in carved torsos from which the stone head and limbs have been broken away (fig. 69). Antique statues recur so often in Titian's paintings that he or anyone of his circle would quite naturally reshape them for figures that were intended to correct—and actually surpassed—the antique knowledge of anatomy. The inspiration of the Antique gave the Vesalian woodcuts a turn of elegance that could have been in Pascal's mind when he remarked that "since we speak of poetical beauty, we should also speak of geometrical beauty and medical beauty which, however, we do not." Pascal acutely picked out the two points, perspective and anatomy, at which science touched art in the Renaissance and the Baroque.

The antique air of the Vesalian muscle men could have gone deeper than taste to warn old-fashioned Galenists: "You are wrong in supposing that man's body has changed since antiquity. Galen merely described it wrongly because he thought it was like the monkeys that he dissected instead of dissecting men." Titian attacked the Galenists directly by parodying the Laocoön group in a woodcut of apes (fig. 73) as if to say: "If in Galen's time men really had had organs like apes, this is how antique statuary would have looked." The point is wittily investigated in Horst W. Jansen's *Apes and Ape Lore*.

Between the two utterly different sets of Vesalian skeletons of 1538 and 1543 lies the gap between the Middle Ages and the Renaissance. The first skeletons in the *Tabulae Sex* of 1538 (fig. 74) are stiff dead things laid out flat for burial, without any suggestion of the dramatic limberness of the second set in the *Fabrica* of 1543 (fig. 70), where there is a vision of the hidden thing that strides and laughs and stretches inside each one of us—a vision of the skeleton as a whole, living a life that even Leonardo perceived only in parts.

The two sets of skeletal woodcuts in the *Tabulae Sex* and the *Fabrica* represent the bones of two different men, so that in the interval between the two books Vesalius may have perfected his invention of articulating bones so as to make them bend in more complex attitudes. Before Vesalius the bones prepared for the classroom stuck springily together by the gristle dried in their joints. Vesalius is the first writer who mentions any method of joining bones together artificially when he says that the *Tabulae Sex* cuts were drawn from "a skeleton recently articulated for the gratification of the curious." Five years later, he illustrated the *Fabrica* with a woodcut showing a tableful of anatomist's instruments, including pincers and two coils of "copper wire for assembling bones." In 1559 Vesalius's method of mounting was minutely described in six folio pages of the anatomy book by Realdo Colombo, who was Vesalius's pupil and successor at Padua. The bones were not linked by metal loops, like today's flexible skeletons, but were strung together

Fig. 72. The Apollo Belvedere. Roman marble copy (about A.D. 130–40),
after a Greek bronze original (about 330 B.C.), attributed to Leochares.
Museo Pio–Clementino, The Vatican, Rome
Alinari/Art Resource, Inc.

Fig. 73. The Laocoön group as monkeys. Woodcut by Niccolo Boldrini after Titian, about 1545.
The Metropolitan Museum of Art, New York. Rogers Fund, 1922

like beads on long wires which were bent to set the skeleton in a fixed attitude. Colombo says that it is handsome to let one arm hang down and crook the other like the skeletons in the *Tabulae Sex*. Wires run through the skeleton (still partly extant) that Vesalius gave to the medical school at Basel in 1542, and appear to do so in the one in the Roman Academy of St. Luke (fig. 58). Vesalius evidently thought that mounting bones was a device too menial to claim as an invention, for Colombo warns his readers, "Do not, like Vesalius, cast these skeletons away as though they were worthless." Colombo's ungenerous account seems to credit Vesalius with the invention when he says that "the good Vesalius never thought of draining the marrow from the bones to keep them from darkening"—as though he had thought of everything else.

Even before the discovery of mounting, an artist could still pose an incomplete skeleton in simple action. A rib cage like the one on the floor of Bandinelli's Academy (fig. 75), could have been laid on its back on a table with a skull and arms propped into position. But it would be very

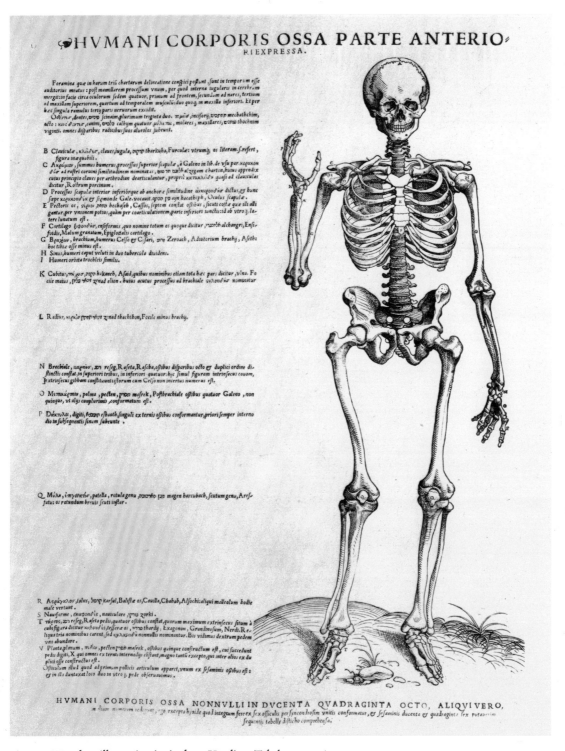

Fig. 74. Woodcut illustration in Andreas Vesalius, *Tabulae anatomicae sex*,
Venice, 1538. (Restrike, 1934).
The Metropolitan Museum of Art, New York. Gift of the New York Academy of Medicine, 1947

Fig. 75. Enea Vico. The Academy of Baccio Bandinelli. Engraving, 1550.
The Metropolitan Museum of Art, New York. Joseph Pulitzer Bequest, 1917

Fig. 76. Woodcut illustration by Michael Wolgemut in Hartmann Schedel's
so-called *Nuremberg Chronicle*, Nuremberg (Koberger), 1493.
The Metropolitan Museum of Art, New York. Rogers Fund, 1921

Fig. 77. The Physician. Woodcut by Hans Franck Lützelburger after
Hans Holbein, the Younger in *The Dance of Death*, Lyons, 1547.
The Metropolitan Museum of Art, New York. Rogers Fund, 1919

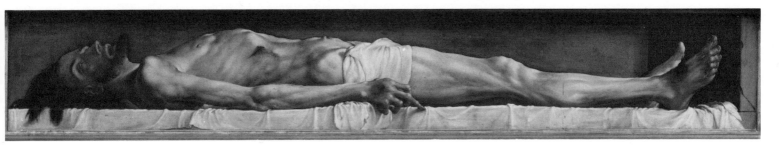

Fig. 78. Hans Holbein. Christ in the Tomb, 1521. Oil and tempera on limewood.
Oeffentliche Kunstsammlung, Kunstmuseum Basel

much harder to prop or hang the unmounted bones of a whole body in the supple poses of the *Fabrica*. Though all of the Vesalian skeletons were drawn from mounted specimens, a more flexible articulation could account in part for the expressiveness of the second set.

It took so long to represent the skeleton correctly because its shapes are so complex. Antique artists had jumbled vague lengths together like bent safety pins (fig. 12) and the Middle Ages did hardly better with the ragged cadavers that jig at the Last Trump (fig. 76), or arrest all conditions of men in the Dance of Death (fig. 71). The subject of the Dance of Death might have been suggested by the playful skeletons that Romans modeled on lamps and drinking cups (fig. 12) to remind them of life's brief candle and to spice their banquets with a pinch of ultimate dust. It would be interesting to know if these lamps and cups were any worse modeled than the jointed silver skeleton that Trimalchio toyed with at his supper of surfeits.

Dried cadavers recur instead of skeletons in mediaeval art because actual ones littered at least one corner of every churchyard and also served teachers to demonstrate anatomy. The most famous pre-Vesalian reminiscence of a mediaeval graveyard is the set of woodcuts of the Dance of Death drawn by Holbein before the publication of the *Fabrica*, though not published until afterward (fig. 77). Even Holbein, usually so accurate, put two bones in the upper arm and one in the forearm. This error, which he could have corrected by merely feeling his own arms, surprises in the artist who was able to paint the most terrifying portrait of a cadaver that exists (fig. 78). The lucid brutality of his *Dead Christ* illustrates Meister Eckhart's saying that, as Christ was the most beautiful man while he lived, so was he the ugliest during his three days of death. After so many able artists had bungled the skeleton for centuries, Leonardo's and Titian's triumphs appear all the more startling.

FIGURE DRAWING AFTER VESALIUS

FIVE YEARS of preparation had alerted people to the publication of the *Fabrica*. One senses the eagerness of anticipation in a letter in the Medici archives (filza 1170, carta 362), written on November 14, 1543 from Poggio by Martio Vescovo, one of Luke Cosimo's secretaries, to the duke's major-domo: "The anatomy book arrived last night and I took it at once to the Duke, who immediately began to study the contents with the Cardinal (Juan Alvarez de Toledo, Cardinal of Burgos). Since the binding was damp, I put the book on a stool with a weight on top to keep it flat." Duke Cosimo's interest continued, for he later helped Vesalius by sending him bodies at Pisa University for demonstrations.

In the same year of 1543 the Church received the *Fabrica* without rebuke, but thundered down the condemnation of the Index on Copernicus's *Revolutions of the Celestial Spheres*. Today both seem to have revised science equally radically, but at the time they looked quite different. When the new astronomy of Copernicus contradicted Genesis by displacing the center of our planetary system from the earth to the sun, it sinned by dethroning man from the center of creation. It did not redeem Copernicus that he should have helped the Church to combat astrology by demonstrating that the now impersonal stars were too remote to connect easily with one's own private fate and the parts of one's body according to the superstition that continued to survive from the Babylonians. The *Fabrica*, on the other hand, centered attention on man, the all-absorbing preoccupation of Greeks and Jews, and hence of Christians. It asked no embarrassing "whence?" or "why?" but simply, "what is it?" It hardly referred to the current physiology of the four humors, took no interest in astrology, philosophy, or theology, and so far from refuting anything of importance in the Bible, it actually instilled a Christian humility by parading man's mortality in tatters. The woodcuts could not have shocked people accustomed to seeing walls painted with the Dance of Death, chapels hung with votive models of Lucy's eyes, Agatha's breasts and Anthony's arms, not to mention cemeteries stinking with actual remains. Vesalius must have been confident that he would not offend the various doctrines that Catholics and Protestants disliked having discussed, for he prepared his book quite openly in a Catholic country and published it in a Protestant one. Nor did he wait like Copernicus for the sanctuary of the deathbed.

The Vesalian woodcuts established a model that other anatomical illustrators could only copy or adapt for more than three centuries, for overnight, anatomy ceased to be Galenic and became forever Vesalian. Such a reversal of tradition naturally drew outcries from old-fashioned anatomists who had memorized Galen instead of exploring the body on their own, and some medical schools clung to Mondino's handier checklist for nearly a century. But the artists found exactly the information that they wanted for a naturalistic style. No artist seems to have opposed the new anatomy except in Spain, where Vesalius himself ran into the only disapproval that ever seriously interfered with his dissections. In Seville in 1585, more than forty years after the *Fabrica*, the sculptor and goldsmith Juan de Arphe published a protest in his *Libro de varia Commensuracion*. As the title suggests, most of its illustrations of anatomy are copied from Dürer's measured drawings and none from Vesalius. The only pictures from life are three woodcuts of the skeleton drawn as Leonardo drew it, from the front, side, and back, which Juan de Arphe says he studied from one of "those complete skeletons that you see in any graveyard." After having studied the bones he thought that he ought to look at dissection, and so went to the University of Salamanca where he watched Dr. Cosme de Medina "skin the bodies of some poor men and women who had been executed. Quite aside from being horrible and cruel, it was not fitting (*decente*) for art because the muscles of the face and belly are mere bumps in sculpture, and the muscles of the arms and legs show clearly in live models." Ruskin expressed the same revulsion when he called dissection "a degradation as well as a hindrance" to the artist, filling "your eyes and memory with horrible things which Heaven never meant you so much as to glance at."

This natural repugnance recommended Calcar's woodcuts still more to artists. Before 1543 an artist had no ready access to muscular structure except through scarce anatomical drawings or the messy drudgery of dissection, but now Calcar's woodcuts gave him a cheaper, readier source of information that artists have used ever since. Thus his illustrations did not stimulate artists to dissect, but discouraged them. The detail and comprehensiveness of his pictures removed the zest of discovery from the Florentine artists who had pioneered in dissecting for over two generations. Even if Michelangelo could have pulled himself together to work on his anatomy book, he must have realized that the world needed it less after 1543 than before. A few artists have nevertheless persevered in making anatomy books. Rubens, for instance, illustrated two unpublished manuscripts, one of which was burned in 1720. But instead of any pictures of dissections, Rubens drew in them copies after antique statues, after Raphael, and after many of the Leonardo drawings that he had seen in Pompeo Leoni's house. Rubens published some separate engravings which he might have intended for a third abortive book. One of these separate prints shows a highly imaginary dissection of hands from Michelangelo's *Slave* and *Moses* (fig. 79), where the swollen turbulence of the muscles flows with such insolent improbability that Rubens cannot have learned much from dissections.

Calcar's woodcuts must have helped to shape the Baroque canon of the figure. More than half a century before the publication of the *Fabrica*, when the Florentines were the only artists who commonly dissected, Botticelli began to play with the lean anatomy of Pollaiuolo by elongating and dislocating the figures. Since every Florentine knew the usual proportions, why not divert oneself with modish oddities? Then Michelangelo, Parmigiano, and Rosso standardized these attenuations into the elegant acrobatics of mannerism. But just when a whole group of young artists in Fontainebleau were carrying the new manner to its limit by stretching necks and

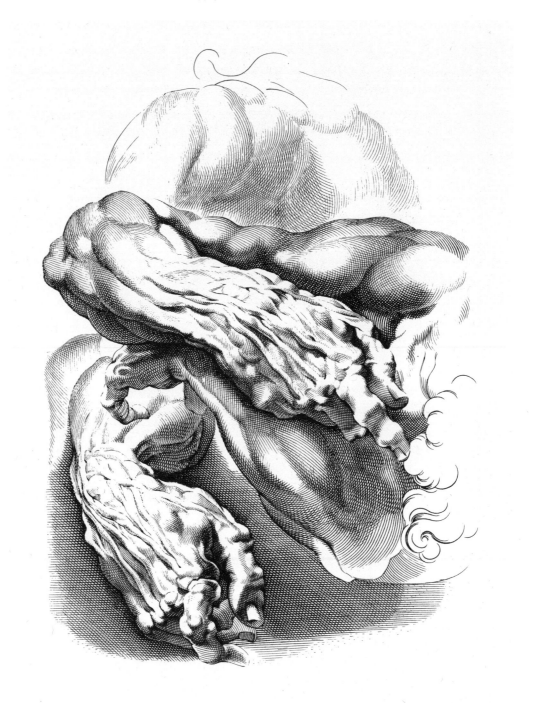

Fig. 79. Illustration for a drawing book engraved after Peter Paul Rubens (1577–1640).
The Metropolitan Museum of Art, New York.
The Elisha Whittelsey Collection, The Elisha Whittelsey Fund, 1951

thighs with really outrageous cunning, Michelangelo's *Last Judgment* and Calcar's woodcuts suddenly dramatized the stocky proportions of Roman statuary. Vesalian authority must have played its part in establishing the heavy-set, muscular figure as normal for Baroque art. Michelangelo helped to popularize both the slender and the stocky proportions because he was such a master of anatomy that he pushed and pulled the figure like an accordion.

It would be interesting to try to sort out the causes that alter human figures in art. Artistic license probably accounts for less than we often assume, for in some periods men and women must actually have looked different. It is probable that European cave men fattened themselves like Eskimo on blubber and grease in order to survive in their colder climate, until they really swelled almost to the bursting fecundity of the women in their prehistoric carvings. Egyptian paintings and Pompeian copies of Greek paintings show tanned men and pale women because in Egypt and Greece the men hunted and farmed and fought under a bright sun while the women kept indoors. In paintings by Tintoretto and other Venetians, occupation must also account for the men with their massive arm muscles and remarkably narrow, almost sunken chests, which could have been formed by years of pulling an oar on a galley or pushing one on a gondola. Any tightness in clothes always constricts the body, as the mediaeval doublet pinched men's waists and the nineteenth-century corset weakened the abdomen and broadened the hips of the women who posed for Courbet and Etty. The oddest source for a human type in art came in the eighteenth century in Paris, where painters and sculptors tended for a long time to represent one general type of body because as students they had got used to the proportions of the one model who had the monopoly of posing at the *Académie's* drawing school for twenty-five years. (He sold his skeleton to the *Académie* to prolong his dominance.) His slender hands and feet, long limbs, and very sloping shoulders appear in every one of Moreau le Jeune's men and women and even in Boucher's Venuses. On the other hand, artistic license must account for the tall, thin figures that the Mannerists and El Greco painted to express an ideal of elegance while actually looking with eyes like yours or mine at men and women shaped as we are. The antique massiveness of the Vesalian figure spread with the spread of the omnivorous, exact researches into every detail of Greece and Rome.

Vesalius's book also gave a new direction to anatomy among the scientists. By adequately answering the question, "How do our bodies look?", it turned science to the next question, which still occupies it: "What do the various parts do?" One of the first men who remarked on the change from gross anatomy to physiology, and the reasons for it, was Francis Bacon. In 1605 he said in his *Advancement of Learning*: "Anatomists inquire of the parts, and their substances, figures, and collocations, but they inquire not of the diversities of the parts, the secrecies of the passages, and the seats or nestlings of the humours, nor much of the footsteps and impressions of diseases; the reason of which omission I suppose to be because the first inquiry may be satisfied with a view

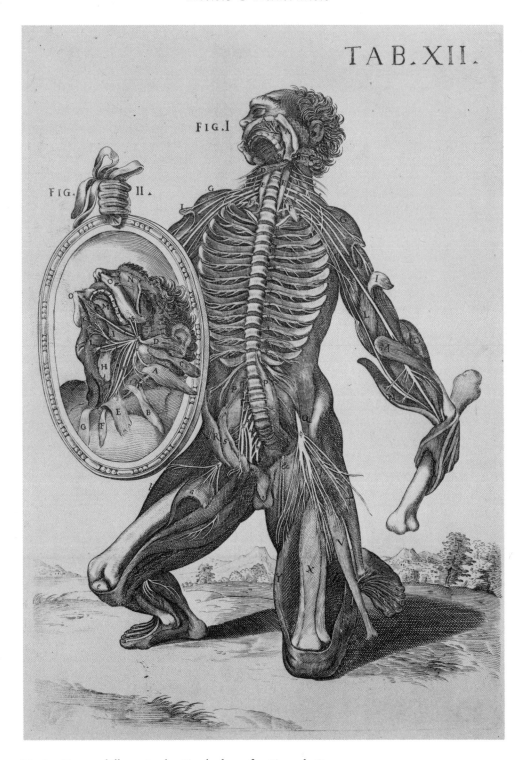

Fig. 80. Engraved illustration by Ciamberlano after Pietro da Cortona
in Petraglia, *Tabulae anatomicae . . .* , Rome, 1788.
The Metropolitan Museum of Art, New York. Gift of Lincoln Kirstein, 1952

Fig. 81. Design for a catafalque. Pisa, about 1740–60. Pencil, ink, and washes.
The Metropolitan Museum of Art, New York.
The Elisha Whittelsey Collection, The Elisha Whittelsey Fund, 1959

Fig. 82. Engraved illustration by Cornelis Huyberts in Frederic Ruysch,
Thesaurus anatomicus, Amsterdam (Wolters), 1703.
The Metropolitan Museum of Art, New York. Gift of Lincoln Kirstein, 1954

Fig. 83. William Hogarth. The Reward of Cruelty, 1751. Engraving.
The Metropolitan Museum of Art, New York.
Harris Brisbane Dick Fund, 1932

of one or few anatomies; but the latter, being comparative and causal, must arise from the view of many."

The new researches into "the secrecies of the passages" produced their first spectacular result in Harvey's discovery of the circulation of the blood, published in 1628. "The footsteps and impressions of diseases" had to wait until 1761 when G. B. Morgagni published the first great morbid anatomy from his many years of dissection at the medical school in Padua. In Bacon's time there was already a beginning of the study of "the diversities of the parts" in books that compared man's anatomy with the other animals, as if to discover a basic design for all vertebrates—a comparison that ultimately produced Darwin's *Origin of Species* in 1859. Hamlet was being as "modern" as Francis Bacon when he referred to his body as "this machine."

The new physiology engaged the last outstanding artist who lent a hand to the advancement of human anatomy. This was Pietro da Cortona, who designed some somber, violent engravings (fig. 80), to illustrate a text that was either never written or is now lost. Though one of Pietro's engravings is dated 1618, they were not published until 1741 with a text written then to explain them. These pictures come out of a world far removed from the Renaissance of Calcar's strutting statues, which refuse to submit to mortality even when stripped down to the bone. Pietro da Cortona's anatomies are not made of marble but of meat, for they belong to the great optical art of the 17th century which created surfaces for the eye to see instead of shapes for the hand to feel. As the suffering, expressive children of the Baroque they writhe in agony, their nerve ends twisting in the raw air. Art, going parallel to anatomy, was also probing deep into the functioning of man in the subtle motivation of Shakespeare's characters and Rembrandt's portrayal of almost imperceptible emotions.

Once gross anatomy had been explored and mapped for good and all, men began to juggle the subject with metaphysical levity. This started in about 1580 when skeletons appeared on the façade and nave of San Lorenzo in Florence swinging scythes with sinister flippancy during funerals staged by the Medici Grand Dukes, who were always interested in anatomy. Near the anatomy school of the Medici university at Pisa there was an exhilarating catafalque overrun by a scrimmage of skeletons cutting capers like schoolboys (fig. 81). In Holland an anatomist astonished Peter the Great with tiny gray gardens confected out of dried veins and tendons, and peopled with fetal skeletons fiddling inaudible jigs (fig. 82). In addition to being studied as a basis for art, bones were used as the actual raw material of art in the skeletal decorations of baroque catacombs. Such was the visual background of Donne's "bracelet of bright hair about the bone." But at last the great age of anatomical discovery receded so far into the past that Hogarth turned it to ridicule (fig. 83). He showed his knowledge of historical anatomy by elevating the professor in a mediaeval high throne like the one in the Mondino woodcut (fig. 21).

Although pictures of many kinds long ago surveyed man's gross anatomy in great detail, some artists have always wanted the direct knowledge that can only come through dissection.

Fig. 84. Rembrandt van Rijn. The Polish Rider, about 1655. Oil on canvas.
The Frick Collection, New York

Fig. 85. Rembrandt van Rijn. Nude seated on a stool, about 1654–56.
Pen and brown ink, wash.
The Art Institute of Chicago

Fig. 86. Théodore Géricault. Academic Study of the Nude, about 1816. Oil on canvas.
Musée des Beaux-Arts, Rouen
Giraudon/Art Resource, Inc.

Fig. 87. Thomas Eakins. The Gross Clinic, 1875–76. Drawing in india ink
after the painting of the same subject.
The Metropolitan Museum of Art, New York. Rogers Fund, 1923

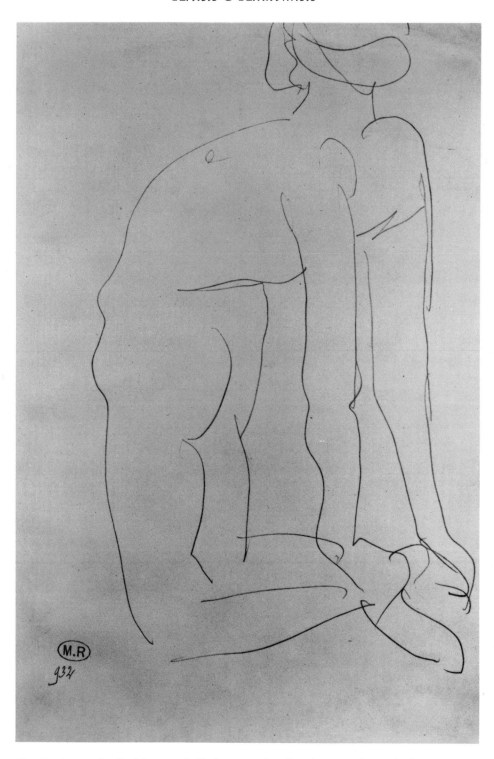

Fig. 88. Auguste Rodin (1840–1917). Nude woman kneeling, her torso thrown back.
Pencil drawing.
Musée Rodin, Paris

Fig. 89. Pablo Picasso. Woman Dressing Her Hair, 1940. Oil on canvas.
Collection of Mrs. Bertram Smith, New York

Rembrandt must have seen a good deal of dissecting while preparing his two anatomy paintings (fig. 40), and he had an amazing eye for the bony scaffolding of the horse and rider (fig. 84). His anatomical studies must have helped him to give the warm compactness, the living bulk to the nudes that he situated in an air as thick as liquid (fig. 85). More recent dissecting shows its results in the young savagery with which Géricault (fig. 86), rebelled against the sleekness and slackness of the drawing schools, and in the painful groping for truth that estranged Thomas Eakins from the politeness of American painting (fig. 87). In 1894 Eakins stated, awkwardly but impressively, the results to be achieved by the artist-dissector: "On the lines of the mighty and simple strains dominating the movement, and felt intuitively and studied out by him, the master artist groups, with full intention, his muscular forms. No detail contradicts. His men and animals live. Such is the work of three or four modern artists. Such was the work of many an old Greek sculptor."

Artists conformed more or less to the Vesalian standard of anatomy just so long as they held to the Florentine invention of mathematical perspective. Then, in about 1900 in Paris, both together collapsed. Rodin started to shift the center of gravity when he drew from the model while hardly glancing at his pencil so as to free his hand for inventing more boldly than it would dare under the constant censure of his eye (fig. 88). His drawings opened a path where many have followed. When Picasso and Matisse began painting a table with legs in elevation and the top in a bird's-eye view, they also began experimenting with figures to subordinate everything to expressive movement. Picasso's excruciatingly maladjusted woman (fig. 89), shocks because the painter has distorted every proportion, every connection with as full a knowledge of anatomy as Polycleitus's when he reshaped nature to suit Greek taste. The modern artists who flexed a leg like macaroni, or put three eyes in a head, or assembled cylinders into a torso were taking liberties quite different from those that Polycleitus took with his torsos, or Ingres with the arms that he pulled out to half again their natural length. The modern distortions express a revolutionary revision of man, or rather a diversity of visions, as artistic styles have ceased to rest on common agreement and have split into a diversity of worlds, along with poetry, music, and geometry.

The pioneers of the early 1900s were free to invent themes on the figure because they had first learned classical anatomy. Because they could draw the figure accurately without the model, they could also dominate a model if they had one posing in front of them, and if they had none, they could plunge into the imagination from a firm springboard of remembered observation. But while figure drawing has been explored to so many personal extremes, some artists felt the need for returning to a classic common ground. In such a movement of return to Vesalian classicism, Tchelitchew made fluorescent portraits of the sinuses (fig. 90), and Dali imagined the ardor of a tibia for a liver (fig. 91). These artists felt the old healthy impulse to investigate, Leonardo's curiosity to strip man down to his secret existence, even though they were not drawing like Leonardo to investigate something undiscovered, but were feeling out their reactions to some

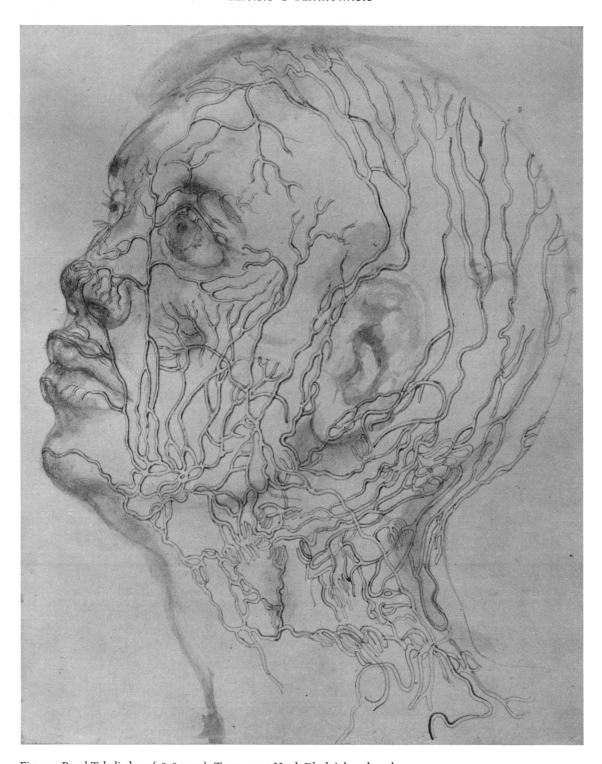

Fig. 90. Pavel Tchelitchew (1898–1957). Transparent Head. Black ink and wash.
The Metropolitan Museum of Art, New York.
Gift of Lincoln Kirstein, 1964

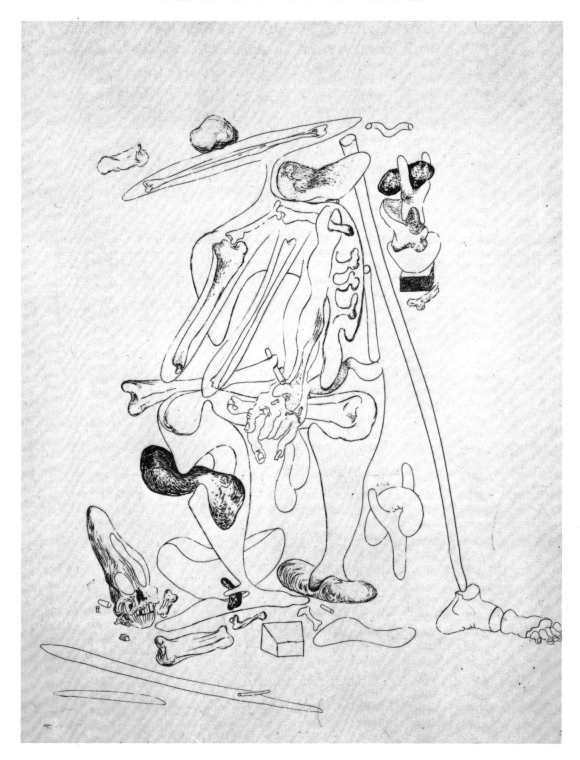

Fig. 91. Salvador Dali. Etching in Comte de Lautréamont, *Les Chants de Maldoror*, Paris (Skira), 1934.
The Metropolitan Museum of Art, New York. Harris Brisbane Dick Fund, 1942

familiar aspect of nature. Science long ago ceased to employ independent artists, ceased to goad the unspecialized painter with that invigorating irritant of necessity that enabled Calcar to rise above his probably middling gifts. The last outstanding artist who gave his great vision to science was probably George Stubbs in his haunting etchings for the *Anatomy of the Horse* in 1766.

As late as the nineteenth century scientists could easily have worked with artists who had broader views than the specialist illustrators, but nowadays, when many scientific discoveries concern processes that cannot be observed directly with the eye, an artist's sharp observation can do less to advance science. But even now an artist could discover visual symbols of invisible phenomena to instruct you and me, and he could help a scientist to a fresh view and perhaps a new start by summarizing his problem in unexpected terms. Looking back, one can imagine the extraordinary pictures that scientific discoveries could have struck from certain artists. Think how Caravaggio, had he not died so young, could have dramatized Harvey's discovery of the age-old riddle of the circulation of the blood, how Tchelitchew could have taken us inside the reckless proliferation of the cancer cells, how Picasso could have made us experience the instant of fission and fusion. But instead, as the wholeness of Renaissance man has been economically cut to pieces to make efficient specialists, scientific illustration has been relegated to departmentalized draftsmen who are more docile for scientists to work with because they do not introduce ideas generated by coping with the wider problems of general picture-making. So today's easel painter never has to undertake those chores of making pictures for special and often trifling needs, chores such as fell to the Renaissance workshops, bringing the stimulus of novelty. As a consequence, science can no longer make you and me imagine the reality of its revelations, and art has lost its intellectual scintillation for, alas, science refuses to look out of her laboratory window and art has shut herself up in her distant and superior studio.

Composed in English Monotype Bembo and
printed by A. Colish, Inc., Mount Vernon, New York.
Designed by Bert Clarke,
with title page lettering by Jerry Kelly.

———————

MCMLXXXIV